Happily Ever After

The ENGAGED COUPLES' GUIDE *to*

Getting Marriage Right

DR. LAWRENCE I. SANK

www.gettingmarriageright.com

Mill City Press, Inc.
322 First Avenue N, 5th floor
Minneapolis, MN 55401
612.455.2293
www.millcitypublishing.com

ISBN-13: 978-1-62652-745-4
LCCN: 2014907401

Edited by Janet Hulstrand
Typeset by James Arneson

Printed in the United States of America

This book is dedicated to my parents, Sydney and Estelle Sank and to my wife, Dr. Carolyn Shaffer. My parents had 59 years together demonstrating a marriage of durability, flexibility and evolution over the decades. They consistently provided me with a sense of True North. Those to whom this book is helpful have my parents to thank.

My own marriage has also inspired me to write this book. I want to share what my wife, also a couples therapist, and I have taught each other during our over 30 years of marriage.

"We must not see ***any*** *person as an abstraction.*
Instead, we must see in every person a universe with its own secrets,
with its own treasures, with its own sources of anguish,
and with some measure of triumph."

—Elie Wiesel

CONTENTS

Introduction

"I used to believe that marriage would diminish me, reduce my options. That you had to be someone less to live with someone else. When, of course, you have to be someone more." — ***Candice Bergen***

Congratulations! Whether you received this book as a gift, bought it, or you're just looking at it casually, you've demonstrated that you are curious about some crucial issues in two of the most important relationships in your life—the one you have with your fiancé, and the one you have with yourself.

Why this book is important...

It's rather ironic that people tend to take better care of their cars than their marriages. Think about it: in preparing for a long automobile trip, all systems—brakes, coolant system, tires, engine, etc.—are checked out and tuned up. People about to embark on a long journey don't want to risk breaking an axle or having a tire blow out somewhere along the way.

Yet most couples, when they are embarking on the journey of a lifetime, don't give their relationship even a quick once-over. Sadly, many of them may even ignore clear warning lights on the metaphorical dashboard before taking their wedding vows.

And of course we know what happens all too often. Taking note of the divorce rate can be alarming: depending on whose figures you use, the divorce rate for first marriages is between 41% and 50%. For second marriages, it's estimated to be 66%, and for third marriages, 75%. Such figures should give anyone pause.

However, to continue with our road-trip analogy, if even a modest investment of time and money were applied to preparing for the marital journey, couples could avoid all kinds of heartache and trouble and avoid either dissolving their marriages, or staying together for life—unhappily. With proper preventive maintenance, the marriage journey could be far safer and more enjoyable.

Another sad irony is the expense put into weddings. Many couples spend tens of thousands of dollars, sparing no expense, perhaps even going into debt. Then, all too often, just a few years later they spend tens of thousands of dollars again, this time on a divorce.

Unfortunately, there's no getting around it. Maintaining a marriage requires work. But it can be very rewarding work; and the work required to maintain a happy home is well worth the effort.

This work includes important skill building, but most of the skills you will work on building and refining in this book you actually started learning back in preschool. (Share. Be polite. Don't cheat. No changing the rules in the middle of the game. No hitting, no lying, no yelling. Take turns. Cooperate. Keep your promises.)

Often the sacrifices and compromises involved in maintaining a healthy marriage become a bit more complicated as the years go by. But as this happens, the basic skills of living in harmony with another person hardly become obsolete: on the contrary they are all the more important.

Marriage will demand many things of you and your partner: you will need to learn how to reflect upon yourself and your own qualities and characteristics, both good and bad. You will need to be able to make a clear-eyed appraisal of your fiancé. Often you will need to learn to accept what *is* rather than insisting on what *"should"* be. The exercises in this book will help you develop and tone the emotional "muscles" you will need to develop as you learn the importance of cooperation and compromise, nonjudgmental analysis, and the hard truth that saying "I'm sorry" or "I didn't mean to hurt your feelings" is often as important as saying "I love you"—and will probably need to be said nearly as often.

Marriage preparation books, and particularly self-help books about marriage, are often too clever by half. And while I wish to make the process of completing this book a pleasant, even an exciting, experience for you, I suspect you will seldom find it amusing. But I do hope you will find the process of working through it to be a provocative and a life-enhancing one, something worthy of your time and attention.

This book is designed to get you to think about some very important parts of you that make you the person you are. You might think of it as an owner's manual. Answering the questions in this book will give you the opportunity to learn more about yourself: it can also lead you into a better understanding of your relationship with your partner.

You might want to skip around from section to section, seeking out whichever topics seem most important or most interesting to you. (Of course, while skipping around is fine, I certainly don't recommend ignoring the troublesome areas—or possibly the frightening or disturbing parts—because that's exactly what this book is designed to help you address.) Trust a seasoned psychologist on this: problems between partners don't just go away on their own. They have a troubling habit of reappearing, sometimes disguised as something else, but always with the same basic core. And usually these problem areas become worse over time, not better.

This book is not intended to be a compatibility quiz. You and your partner have already made the decision to be together. I think of it more as a vehicle to help enhance your compatibility. Please be aware as you answer the questions in this book that ***there are no right answers***. These questions are simply designed to help you and your partner understand yourselves and each other better.

Occasionally you may come to an impasse, where your ideas about right and wrong clash strongly with those of your partner. If so, a timely visit to a trusted advisor (a psychologist, marriage counselor, member of the clergy, friend, or relative) may be helpful.

Even if you learn in the course of answering these questions that you disagree about a very important or fundamental issue, it need not be calamitous to your relationship. It may instead become an opportunity to work things out, to express your feelings, to learn more about each other, and to develop an essential skill for all couples: learning how to disagree harmoniously.

Discovering your areas of disagreement and working through them can make way for new growth. "This is how I feel, this is what I believe" need not (and should not) imply "This is how ***you*** should feel or believe." ***Your bond with each other will NOT be strengthened by giving up your individuality or your own personal beliefs and preferences.*** Let this be a guiding principle.

This book is the distilled result of decades of work I've done as a psychologist working with couples. Some of the couples I've worked with had long histories with each other; others were just starting out in their married lives. Some came to me with serious problems that led to the end of the relationship; others merely needed a "tune-up," and returned to living "happily ever after" with each other.

This book is not meant to be a do-it-yourself project for seriously troubled couples. (Seriously troubled couples should probably seek professional advice or assistance.) Rather it is intended to help you and your partner avoid the very common scenario in which little problems between partners grow bigger and bigger. I hope you will consider this as something you'll want to refer to from time to time, and maybe add to, through the years of your marriage.

Some words about format...

Each chapter will be briefly introduced and will then be followed by an illustrative vignette. These vignettes describe composites of actual couples. However, details have been altered to protect each individual's identity. The process described in each vignette addresses but one aspect of each possible problem area and one couple's attempt to grapple with it. This description and its process of resolution are not meant to suggest that the mechanism is the only suitable way to proceed. Following each vignette will be questions that form the heart of the book. They will allow you, the reader, to address each of the topics both thoughtfully and candidly.

I have arranged the topics into general categories; each topic begins with a brief explanation, followed by questions and space to reply. Feel free to elaborate on additional pages that you can append at the end, and to highlight the questions that you consider exceptionally revealing or important to you either individually or as a couple. Perhaps these are areas you will wish to return to or to be certain to discuss with your partner.

As you answer these questions, please take your time, and enjoy the process. Feel free to mix humor, warmth, soul-searching, and don't be afraid of ambiguity! It's okay to be uncertain about some of the answers to these questions; in fact anyone who is really being honest will find him or herself hard put to know how to answer at least some of them.

I hope that the questions in this book, and your responses to them, will come to be the topic of important and illuminating conversations with your future partner. The importance of this process of discussion and self-disclosure cannot be underestimated. This book is truly about you. I hope it will help you dive deep into yourself, and that it will help you engage in an exhilarating process of self-discovery. And that perhaps, when the questions are sufficiently probing, the process will also become a catalyst for personal growth.

As you reply to the questions in this book, we will become in a sense its co-authors. I will be your guide and hopefully will inspire you to think about who you really are and what you want your future life to be like; but only you can truly delve inside yourself, contemplate these questions deeply, learn what there is to know about yourself, and reveal what's important to reveal. Therefore *you* will control the content and the tone of this work. It will be up to you to decide whether you wish to take a light and breezy tone or a more serious one.

You can choose to share the contents of this book with your partner. Or your answers to the questions can remain completely private: they need not be shared with anyone unless you want to share them.

However, I hope this journey of self-discovery will make you want to share these revelations with your partner, and that it may spur you to work on areas that hold the promise of growth for the two of you as a couple.

Dr. Lawrence Sank
Bethesda, Maryland
June, 2013

Author's Note:
An asterisk (*) appears next to those items that seem to not include same-sex or transgendered couples. It is not my intent to exclude anyone. If this applies to you, please change the heterosexual language in the text to match your situation. Similarly, for the sake of consistency the word "fiancé" has been spelled with one "e" at the end: this is not to imply that this workbook is for future brides only! I hope many future grooms will participate in this process of self- and partner-discovery as well.

Day To Day

Early Birds and Night Owls

"Early to bed and early to rise makes a man healthy, wealthy and wise…" — Benjamin Franklin

"If people were meant to pop out of bed, we'd all sleep in toasters." Author unknown

It's remarkable how some of the most mundane factors define who we are. It is also remarkable how the day-to-day details of our lives can make for harmony or dissonance in a relationship.

The times of day when we are most alert, happy, and productive can affect not only the individual choices we make in our day-to-day lives; they can also have a lot to do with how well we mesh as a couple.

The predisposition to be a "morning person" or a "night person" is for some people a strong and in-born tendency, and for those people, it may be very hard to change. For others, it may be possible and desirable to make changes in one's own sleeping habits in order to accommodate a partner's patterns and needs.

Regardless of whether change is needed or desirable, our sleeping habits can affect such things as when and how often we make love; our choice and timing of recreational and leisure activities (matinee vs. late show, day game vs. night game, night-clubbing vs. early morning hikes); our choice of friends; and even our career choices. (Some people are just not able to adjust well to a 9-5 workday.)

But, in our sleeping habits as in so many areas of daily life, it's not the fact, or even the magnitude of our differences, but how we choose (or learn) to deal with them that can make or break a marriage.

LYNN AND JOHN

John had always found it very hard to get going in the morning. He had deliberately chosen his college major and his jobs based on whether they allowed for a later-in-the-day start time. He couldn't remember a time in his life when morning was his friend. This had been a source of worry to his parents. They asked themselves if he'd ever "make it" in this world. But John was studious, hardworking, and resourceful. He ultimately found a teaching position in a university that allowed him to teach afternoon and evening classes. A perfect fit. And it was at the university that John met Lynn. She was taking John's course to get an advanced certificate. The rest is history...except that Lynn was not a late riser.

Lynn was actually a morning person. She, too, was a teacher. She taught at a local high school and was ambitious enough to be taking night courses to improve her salary and to enhance opportunities for moving into administration. As a teacher, Lynn reluctantly acknowledged that her students who seemed half asleep (and some, literally, sound asleep) fell in her esteem. She believed that these students were poorly motivated, unambitious, and not deserving of any special attention or dispensation.

The disparity in energy levels by time of day between John and Lynn was evident from the start. However, it never struck them, even as they dated more seriously, that this would be a problem in their marriage.

The difference was most evident when they took their first vacation together (a Caribbean cruise). Lynn was eager to get an early start. She wanted to be in the gym by 8:00 AM and be off sightseeing by 10 o'clock. John thought 10 o'clock was a bit early...to wake up.

As their devotion to each other grew, Lynn's intolerance for what she called "John's waking problem" also grew. She begged him to talk with a sleep specialist. John was willing, and the doctor suggested that John might actually have a sleep disorder. As a first-line approach the specialist recommended a light box for daily use. Remarkably, John's "problem" gradually resolved. Lynn was very pleased: and as a side benefit, she became more compassionate towards her sleepy students as well.

What time do you usually go to sleep? ____________________

When do you *prefer* to go to sleep? ____________________

How does your vacation sleep schedule differ from your workday sleep schedule? ____________________

____

Do you have any nighttime rituals? (How do you prepare yourself for sleep? e.g., reading, exercising, prayer, making phone calls, watching TV, etc.) Y/N____Please explain____________

____

Would you describe yourself as a light sleeper (i.e., easily awakened) or a sound sleeper? __________

____

Do you have any unusual sleep habits (sleepwalking, sleep-talking, snoring, teeth grinding, dramatic tossing and turning)? Y/N___ Please explain____________________

____

Do you know if your partner is a light sleeper or a sound sleeper? Y/N____

If your partner is a light sleeper, which of your sleep habits might create problems for him or her?

____

How do you like to be awakened? (Gradually, with an alarm clock or radio? With the turning on of lights? By opening the curtains?)____

What do you want your partner to know about your preferences in your bed/bedroom/sleep environment (e.g., size of bed, type of bed, side of bed, light and noise level in bedroom)?________

____

____

Which are preferences and which are mandatory?______________________________________

What do you like to wear to bed? ____

What do you like to do upon awakening when you are not pressed for time? (e.g., stay in bed, catnap, eat breakfast in bed, get up right away) ____

Is there anything your partner will need to do to adjust or conform to your sleep habits? ____

Do you foresee needing to change anything in your habits to accommodate your partner? Y/N____

What changes do you think might be necessary? ____

If so, are you willing to make those changes? Y/N ____

A Question of Taste: Food

"Nothing would be more tiresome than eating and drinking if God had not made them a pleasure as well as a necessity." — Voltaire

What could possibly be problematic between couples when it comes to food? After all, isn't virtually everybody in favor of it?

When it comes to food, the problems tend to revolve around the topics of quality, quantity, and predictability. And because many of our ideas about food are formed early in life and may be deeply rooted, what we eat, how much we eat, and our ideas about mealtime can actually be lightning-rod issues for some couples.

We usually know our own habits and preferences pretty well. It's good to become more aware of how strongly we feel about our own preferences and how tolerant we can be of our mate's.

JODIE AND HARPER

Jodie was, by her own description, a "foodie." Harper was a meat, potatoes, and snacks kind of guy. Quite in contrast to his fiancée, he was not into food, neither its preparation nor the enjoyment of it. In brief, he "ate to live" and Jodie would agree that she "lived to eat." One might ask what it is that they did, then, for a good time? Well, there were many, many overlapping interests: love of the outdoors and vigorous exercise, the theater, and politics. (They had actually met at a political fundraiser.)

The food dilemma, for Jodie, boiled down to the issues of time and money. Harper wanted to spend less of both on food-related activities and Jodie, more. With the assistance of a single consultation with a psychologist, this potential area of discord actually afforded Harper the opportunity to give these two precious commodities to Jodie. By agreeing to spend more time and money on food-related activities, he demonstrated his commitment to the relationship. Harper's "sacrifice" in this regard made Jodie feel more loved and less intently focused on pursuing her passion for food. This lesson in conflict resolution, she later wrote to me, provided an excellent template for other bumps in the road they encountered in their relationship.

How would you describe your eating habits and preferences?

Frequency (three "square meals" a day? more frequent? less frequent? variable?) ______________

____

Amount (substantial, moderate, small) ________________________________

Choices (limited vs. extensive) ____________________________________

Presentation (formal or informal? i.e., straight from the stove-top/microwave, or from serving dishes, on fine china?) ____

Setting (table with place settings, standing at counter, while reading, watching TV, or listening to music?) ____________________

Variety (Do you prefer predictability or experimentation when it comes to meals?)

____Predictability ____Experimentation Please explain: ____________________

Do you have food restrictions? Y/N____Please explain your concerns:

Allergies / health ____________________

Religious (e.g., kosher, halal) ____________________

Ethical/health (vegetarian, vegan) ____________________

Aesthetic (foods I just can't stand) ____________________

Other ____________________

How would you describe your general attitude toward eating?

____ Eat to live ____ Live to eat ___Somewhere in between

How would you describe *your partner's* general attitude toward eating?

____ Eat to live ____ Live to eat ___Somewhere in between

How important to you is it that your partner shares your needs/preferences about food?

____

Do you currently, or have you ever had, any emotional issues related to eating or dieting? Please include such things as bulimia, anorexia, extreme dieting, purging/spitting, etc.) Y/N____Please explain. ____________________

____

Do you have any strong feelings about food preparation and clean-up (who does it? when does it happen, etc.)? ____________________

A Question of Style (Clothing, Fashion, Interior Design)

"Fashion is a form of ugliness so intolerable that we have to alter it every six months." — Oscar Wilde

This quip may apply to many couples. However, it doesn't help much in those cases where there may be a conflict over not just *what* is fashionable, but whether there should be any attention *at all* paid to fashion. In those cases, addressing the conflict can begin with trying to understand just how profound, and deep-seated, your differences may be, and finding a way to respect those differences.

For some couples it may not be so much a difference in taste, as a difference of opinion about whether being "in fashion" is worth the high cost of being fashionable. For example, some couples may have serious disagreement about the amount of money and time that should be spent on shopping, grooming, etc. For other couples, space issues may arise about where to put all those clothes.

Other couples may clash over their conflicting tastes: is a bright color scheme "cheerful" or "in bad taste"? Does being in fashion mean being up-to-date, or is it more about having a general approach to the way you present yourself that is aesthetically pleasing? Should fashion play a major role in decisions made about the clothing and shoes we wear, or is functionality—comfort, practicality, etc.—more important?

As in any other area of life where there are significant differences of opinion or approach, it's not so much the differences you discover as the way you and your partner deal with those differences that matters. Working out cooperative solutions to the problems raised by your differences can make each of you more interesting, tolerant, well-rounded people: failure to do so may give rise to a festering source of resentment, embarrassment, and pain.

A fundamental underlying question that arises when we think about clothing and fashion is the notion of the importance of identity. How much are we willing to cede our own preferred way of doing things, or expressing ourselves, in order to accommodate our partner's preferences? When is fashion an essential expression of our inner selves, and when is it just "window dressing?" (Or, as Jerry Seinfeld once said in a different context, is it all "just laundry?") How much does the way I dress matter to my being me? Will I lose myself if I have to give up my signature unmatched socks or my plunging neckline?

Again, these questions have no right or wrong answers. But they are all good questions to ask.

FRED AND STEPHANIE

Fred felt Stephanie dressed too provocatively when they went out. She, on the other hand, believed that showing off her legs or cleavage was appropriate for her age and figure in certain settings. This wasn't an insurmountable disagreement to have except... they didn't have it. Fred was reluctant to bring up the topic. He feared he'd give the impression that he was a prude. He also didn't want to be perceived as questioning

> Stephanie's judgment or, worse, her commitment/fidelity to their status as an engaged couple. But all Stephanie observed was that Fred seemed uneasy when they went out, as if he had a problem being sociable. He didn't seem as much fun as he used to be. He seemed very clingy. He was not at all the self-assured guy she thought she knew so well. Happily, at long last, Stephanie pressed Fred to talk to her about his "anxiety." After some initial evasion, he screwed up his courage and spoke his mind. Stephanie, happily, was able to understand Fred's objection to her style of dress. She was even a bit pleased that he was being somewhat possessive. They agreed that in the future she'd consult with him about what she wore.

Using the scale below, indicate how important your choice of clothing and sense of fashion is to you:

Not important — Very important

1 2 3 4 5 6 7 8 9 10

On this same scale, how important is this for your partner? ____________________

What role do you wish to play in your partner's clothing/fashion choices? ____________________

____

What role do you wish to allow your partner in your clothing/fashion choices? ____________

Using the following scale, indicate how you regard your style of dress regarding modesty:

Conservative — Provocative/revealing

1 2 3 4 5 6 7 8 9 10

Your manner of dress____

Your partner's manner of dress____

Using the scale above:

How would you prefer that your partner dress?____________________________

How comfortable are you with the way your partner dresses?____________________

How comfortable is your partner with the way you dress? ____________________

Using the scale below, indicate how you wish the decisions to be made about:

Interior decoration ____ Architectural design ____ Landscaping ____ Choice of home ____ Choice of car ____

Solely by me — Solely by mate

1 2 3 4 5 6 7 8 9 10

Do you tend to hire or engage "consultants" (e.g., relative, interior designer, friend) to help with these things? Y/N ____

Whom would you choose to help you if you were to seek assistance with these decisions?________

How do you think your partner would feel about this?____

Can you describe in a sentence or two how important the way things look is to you? Why is it important for your partner to understand how you feel about this?____________________________

____

____

Free Time: Enjoying Time Together...

"A simple enough pleasure, surely, to have breakfast alone with one's husband, but how seldom married people in the midst of life achieve it." — Anne Morrow Lindbergh

Downtime is a precious resource. Even the briefest periods of "play" time offer opportunities to reconnect with your partner. Whether that time is used for lighthearted silliness or dedicated practice, such as for a tournament or marathon, a couple engaged together in leisure-time activities (non-income producing, non-obligatory, fully voluntary) is making an important investment in their relationship.

Even "parallel play" activities (reading, watching movies, knitting, performing charitable acts, crossword puzzles) can be rejuvenating for a couple. Of course, for some, the more interactive the activity (tennis, board games), the better.

Playtime together promotes relationship building. These times can remind you of why you got together in the first place and how and why you enjoy being in each other's presence.

Activities that you prefer to do alone, in which you may find you are merely tolerating your partner's presence, or activities which your partner doesn't really enjoy, are probably activities better done alone. There's nothing wrong with that! Couples need both alone time and together time. (See also "Independence/Dependence.")

GREG AND ALICE

Both Greg and Alice well understood the concept of balancing free time spent alone and free time spent together. However, Greg felt a gnawing sense of guilt every time he chose the former. He imagined that Alice would sulk when he explained that he wanted to go to the driving range alone or take a solitary walk around their neighborhood. Alice sensed Greg's uneasiness and went out of her way to reassure Greg that she welcomed his choices. However, Greg never caught Alice choosing to be alone during her free time. Therefore, he continued feeling guilty. Actually, Alice didn't feel much need to have solitary time. She described herself as a people person. Being with others, especially Greg, left her feeling recharged. In contrast, too much people-time would leave Greg feeling depleted. What ultimately convinced Greg that he had a problem was when he recognized that he felt guilty even when leaving their cat alone. Greg couldn't bear pushing Felix off his lap when he decided to leave the room or change his seated position. Even Greg had to concede that this had gone too far. He began requesting alone time for himself. He recognized that this was a healthy choice both for himself and for Alice.

Describe what you would consider the best way to spend:

A free afternoon together ______________________________

A free day together ______________________________

A free weekend together ______________________________

How do you imagine your choices would differ from your partner's? ______________________________

____

____

How would you like to reconcile these differences?______________________________

Using the scale below, how would you describe your general energy level? ______

Low Energy									High Energy
1	2	3	4	5	6	7	8	9	10

Using the same scale, how would you describe your partner's energy level? ______

Is there a significant difference in the energy level of you and your partner? If "yes," how important is this difference? Are you concerned that it may cause problems in your marriage? How do you propose to reconcile this difference? ______________________________

And Enjoying Time Apart...

"Together you shall be forevermore...But let there be spaces in your togetherness,
And let the winds of the heavens dance between you..." — *Kahlil Gibran*

You don't have to spend all your free time together, and in fact, it's probably not a good idea to try to do so. A relationship can be strengthened when each partner brings his own unique interests, even passions, into the relationship.

Whether your passions are sports, opera, volunteering, or candle making, each of you is entitled to maintain your own separate interests and to engage in time spent away from each other.

Of course, it's important to ensure that your individual interests don't take over all your spare time, or encroach on your opportunities for spending time together as a couple, or get in the way of major obligations (career, household chores, parenting). Learning how to prioritize and make good choices about how we spend our time is important for all individuals and couples.

In a healthy marriage, balancing the ratio between "me time" and "we time" is an important, sometimes essential, consideration. And recalibrating this ratio from time to time, working with your partner, is an important part of the ongoing work of a relationship.

Describe those things you enjoy doing *separate from* your partner. ____________________

____

____

____

What qualities do these activities bring out in you? Why do you find them enjoyable? ________

____

Do you hope to keep these activities as a vital part of your life post-marriage? Y/N ____

If "yes," how can you keep them from encroaching on couple time? ____________________

____

____

Is there anything about these activities that might weaken your relationship? Y/N ____

Please explain____

____

How can you reduce these risks?____

Does your partner have any activities that don't include you, that might make you feel left out? Y/N ____ If yes, please explain.____

____

____

Do you have any suggestions as to how this potential problem could be avoided? Y/N ____

Please explain____

Potentially Annoying Habits

"Keep the eyes wide open before marriage and half shut afterwards." — Benjamin Franklin

Everybody has their funny little quirks, and usually our own habits seem innocent enough to us. In fact, unless they have been mentioned to us by others (family, close friends, roommates), we might not even realize we have them. At other times, we might suspect these habits are not so benign after all, but they are very hard to contain.

But because "one man's meat is another man's poison," it can be helpful to examine our own personal habits and think about whether any of them might seem odd or might irritate our partner or cause a problem over time. (Don't worry; the process of sharing this, too, can actually bring you closer.)

TREVOR AND ALLISON

Trevor saved cash register receipts. This habit started as a reasonable approach to helping him keep to a budget when he was a struggling college student. But that habit continued for the dozen years thereafter. At age 31 he had accumulated several thousand receipts—all on paper, all in shoeboxes, neatly labeled by month and year. Trevor felt that although this collecting was not necessarily useful, it was also a rather benign habit. "Who does it hurt?" he asked rhetorically. His fiancée, Allison, first stumbled upon this collection while helping Trevor retrieve some luggage from his storage area and was troubled by her "find." She had read about hoarding and had seen a couple of TV reality shows about it. She said she wasn't "freaked out," but she was definitely uneasy about the many, many shoeboxes filled with what she called "nonsense." She wondered what might be "wrong" with Trevor.

Trevor's collection became a source of contention. Allison wanted Trevor to "get help." Trevor contended there was nothing wrong with him and he didn't need help. By way of compromise, the couple agreed to research the topic online. Trevor purchased a self-help book with a relevant title, and they both agreed to read it. As a result of their reading, Trevor agreed that he might have a problem as he came to recognize that he had other collecting behaviors. He doggedly followed the book's suggestions, and in just a few weeks he successfully discarded his various "collections." He didn't find this an easy process. But he did feel a sense of relief once the collections were gone and he felt like he had control of his collecting behaviors. Allison also felt a strong sense of relief, as well as gratitude and appreciation for what Trevor had done in response to her concerns.

For this section, think about comments that friends or family have made about your idiosyncrasies and habits and put those items in the list below.

Describe any "quirks" of yours that others might find irritating, weird, or strange. Some examples might be: I can never wear red, I can never seem to be on time, I always pack too much, I hate it when my vegetables touch the other food on my plate, I have a fear of escalators, I have to toss and turn for a while every night before I can go to sleep, I have to check to see that the door is locked exactly four times before going to bed, etc.______________________________________

____

____

____

Would you be willing to change any of the above habits if they troubled your partner? Y/N ___ If yes, which ones would you be willing to change? In what way? How would you go about doing so?______

____

____

Does your partner have any idiosyncrasies that you would like him or her to change? Y/N ___

If yes, please list:____

____

____

____

How do you plan to ask your partner to make changes in his or her behavior?______________

____

____

____

____

How would you want to be asked to change? ____________________________________

Punctuality: It's About Time

"I owe all my success in life to having been always a quarter of an hour before my time." — Lord Nelson

"Punctuality is the virtue of the bored." — Evelyn Waugh

As with many great men (and women), many partners have differences of opinion about the importance of punctuality. (Trust me, this is a very common problem.) Whether it's about making it on time to the movies, to the airport, or to dinner in a restaurant, this can be a very contentious topic: but it is also one that is better aired and, hopefully, resolved now rather than after your wedding.

Hint: If you and your partner are on opposite ends of this scale, it's probably best not to go into your discussion expecting your partner to change completely. You might want to think about how you can each move a little bit toward the middle, how you can better tolerate each other's differences in this regard, and what steps you can take to minimize daily friction.

BILLY AND MARIE

Billy and Marie had very different views when it came to punctuality. Billy believed that being just on time wasn't good enough. To be suitably respectful to others, he felt an obligation to be early. He also felt better about himself when he arrived extra early for train, bus, and plane departures, restaurant reservations, movies, etc. He enjoyed the experience of being punctual and found being late or having to rush to an appointment very nerve-racking. When facing unexpected traffic problems or other kinds of impediments to his timely arrival, Billy became anxious and irritable.

Marie understood the merit of not keeping others waiting and not missing planes and the beginnings of plays and movies. However, she was far, far more relaxed about being punctual than Billy was. Marie was very determined not to "waste" her time by being early. She also reasoned that she wouldn't be upset when others inadvertently kept her waiting, so why would they get overwrought if she, unintentionally, were to keep them waiting for her?

These differing styles and attitudes toward punctuality led to some pretty harsh quarrels between Marie and Billy. Each insisted on the rightness of their respective positions. Though this did not degrade into name-calling, it was headed in that direction. Fortunately in their premarital meetings, their officiant raised the topic of "areas of discord." The principle of gift-giving and generosity arose, not in the form of tangibles, but something more substantial and difficult. And they got it! Marie recognized the need Billy had for punctuality and could see that greater effort on her part was something she could give him. The change in her attitude wasn't a matter of who was right. The effort was her gift to him. Billy began to regard the effort involved in relaxing his insistence on punctuality as a commitment to Marie and their life together. This was not easy for either of them in practice, but it became easier over time and was an important element in the development of a deeper commitment to and understanding of each other.

Very Punctual/ Usually Early									Consistently Not Punctual/ Usually Late
1	2	3	4	5	6	7	8	9	10

Using the above scale, in general how punctual are you for appointments? ____________

Using the same scale, how would you describe your partner's punctuality, in general? ________

Very Important									Not Important
1	2	3	4	5	6	7	8	9	10

Using the above scale, describe your feelings about the importance of punctuality.__________

Using the above scale, describe your partner's feelings about punctuality ____________

If you have differences in this area, how do you propose to reconcile them? ____________

____

A Question of Dignity: Privacy

"Privacy—like eating and breathing—is one of life's basic requirements." — *Katherine Neville*

In terms of intimacy, there are basically two general categories of privacy: physical (e.g., modesty about our bodies) and emotional (e.g., the contents of our diaries, e-mail, private conversations, etc.). Then there is also privacy that has to do with other things: financial matters, or the details of friends' and families' lives, for example.

Dressing and undressing, personal grooming (e.g., applying makeup), and bathroom activities (showering, use of toilet facilities) are for some people very private matters: others are completely unconcerned about being observed when engaging in these activities. The area of emotional privacy may include various sensitive areas, from personal correspondence and e-mails to a person's financial circumstances (past and present) and family secrets.

You and your partner may have similar beliefs and values about privacy, or you may not.

Again, there's no right or wrong here. It's a question of finding out what you and your partner are comfortable with, respecting your individual differences, and finding a way to cooperate so that you can live happily together as a couple.

HERNAN AND SUZANNE

Hernan was scrupulous about respecting Suzanne's privacy. Though they lived together and shared their innermost thoughts, fears, aspirations, and beliefs, he adamantly insisted upon keeping his correspondence private, even from Suzanne. Hernan described this right to privacy as a matter of "dignity." This felt like a bit of a stretch for Suzanne. She wasn't at all careful about leaving letters on her desk or opened e-mails on her computer. Her feeling was, if she and Hernan were to be as one, then why should she be protective of her correspondence? And why should Hernan be so protective of his? This disparity began to eat at Suzanne. She began to wonder: Did Hernan have something to hide? Like an ex-girlfriend, an online dating service, a porn website subscription? She asked Hernan to be as disclosing to her as she had been to him (i.e., totally). He, predictably, refused.

Suzanne asked her friends for their perspective on this area of disagreement. She even asked Hernan's parents. This last approach was illuminating. Hernan's parents explained in painful detail how Hernan's older brothers had humiliated him when he was in middle school. They were both in tears as they recounted that Hernan wrote in a journal about the "private matters" of a 14-year-old. He wrote about his crushes, his fears, his sexual curiosity. His brothers came upon these entries, scanned them, and posted them on the Internet. Hernan had been understandably humiliated and had refused to return to school. Fortunately, this had happened toward the end of the school year. Still, Hernan had spent a miserable summer with barely any social contacts.

> Happily, when he returned to school in the fall, he seemed to have put this gruesome episode behind him. But thereafter, Hernan's demand for privacy was adamant and was completely and scrupulously respected.
>
> Now that she understood the source of Hernan's insistence on maintaining his privacy, Suzanne was able to put the issue to rest. There was no more suspicion and no more inquiries, just love and understanding.

What areas of your life do you consider to be very private? Indicate with a check mark those things you wish to keep to yourself. Please explain or provide additional detail in the spaces provided after each checked item.

☐ Journals / diaries ____________________

☐ Phone conversations ____________________

☐ Mail / e-mail / texts ____________________

☐ Websites visited (including social media) ____________________

☐ Bathroom / personal hygiene (Do you mind if your partner sees you brush your teeth/bathe/use the toilet/apply makeup?) ____________________

☐ Family secrets (When is it okay to keep a family secret? When is it not?) ____________________

____

____

☐ Doodling, drawing, writing ____________________

☐ Finances: self/others (family) ____________________

What financial information do you consider private information that you don't want to share with anyone, including your partner? ____________________

What financial information do you consider private information that you don't want to share with people other than your partner? ____________________

Are there are any other matters that you consider to be very private?

☐ Other __________ Explain ____________________

☐ Other __________ Explain ____________________

Describe your feelings about nudity (please include time and setting):

Your own nudity ____________________

Your partner's nudity ____________________

A Question of Duty: Chores

"There is no large and difficult task that can't be divided into little, easy tasks." — Buddhist saying

If chores were fun, we'd probably call them hobbies. (But that's another section). Unfortunately, grownups can't indulge in their hobbies and leisure time activities until the chores are done; that's just life.

For some couples, the division of labor reflects traditional societal norms.* For example, he takes care of the lawn, the cars, and the garbage; she takes care of the kitchen, the dusting, and vacuuming.

But many of those traditional gender-specific stereotypes are falling apart in today's two-career families. Things can also change when children enter the picture or when there are tasks that don't easily fall into neat categories. Sometimes this can lead to disagreements about who should do what, and whether the labor is being evenly distributed.

One solution for some couples is to list all the tasks they have to take care of, and then each of them volunteers to take on the ones they would prefer to do, regard as the less unattractive, or the ones they're better suited for by temperament, body size, skill level, and/or availability of time. (For example, one of you may prefer to clean the bathrooms, shop, repair things, etc. The other may be better suited to taking care of paying the bills, preparing the taxes, organizing family activities, etc.)

Other couples may agree on set periods of time during which they take turns with the chores that neither one really wants to do. Some couples are organized and extremely egalitarian. They make up a schedule of who does what, when, making sure that nobody gets stuck with the "nasty" jobs, and that both partners share equally in all aspects of the work of running a home.

Still other couples never talk about this and follow a very loose, laissez-faire approach to household tasks and chores. (Sometimes this works out beautifully; for other couples it can lead to periodic blow-ups, or to an unhealthy, smoldering resentment.)

Of course, there are other ways of resolving the issue of the assignment of tasks, including flipping coins, hiring outside help, or arguing about it all the time (Note: The latter is ***not*** recommended.)

Whatever method you choose, regular re-evaluation of the plan you have made *is* recommended. This is because frequently, as a couple's situation changes, so do the agreements about domestic chores. What's most important is to make sure that there is an understanding that the burden of work needs to be fairly divided in some way, and to ensure that both members' contributions to the household are acknowledged and appreciated.

Often a major pitfall in the assignment of tasks is encountered when one or both partners insist upon making an arrangement that is absolutely "fair." My very best advice to any couple in this regard may be seen as contradictory. My advice is that if you want to work well together you should:

- Stop keeping track (as in "keeping score") of who's doing what, especially when you're feeling overwrought or cranky.
- Make sure that you yourself do *at least* 55% of the household tasks eagerly and graciously.
- Neither expect nor insist upon "payback" for the "extra" 5% you have done.

If it turns out that one person is doing almost all of the work, or that the arrangement is turning out to be consistently much more like 70/30, this is not a good situation and calls for a meeting to work out a more equitable arrangement.

However you end up deciding to divide household and other tasks, the process can start with your responses to the following questions and the sharing of these responses with your partner.

AUSTIN AND MELANIE

Austin and Melanie had been living together for several months. Their pattern for housekeeping did not seem to be working—at least insofar as Austin was concerned. Melanie was not nearly as tidy as his mother. For example, she left dishes in the sink and her underwear hanging in the bathroom. Melanie was somewhat sympathetic to Austin's complaint, but pointed out that his mom did not work out of the home and was what Melanie privately called "anal." In contrast, Melanie was in a very demanding doctoral program that took up altogether too much of her time. She felt overwhelmed and did not take kindly to Austin's criticism. Especially, as she reminded him, when Austin had a far more orderly life as a computer programmer with set hours and few overtime demands.

Melanie and Austin weren't shy about this conflict. Fortunately they had discussed this with Austin's older sister. She listened sympathetically and wisely recommended that they both back off from insisting on extracting a change in the other. Being in a relationship, she advised, doesn't give you free rein to change your partner, but to love him/her and, perhaps, even celebrate the differences. This wisdom sobered up both Melanie and Austin, leaving them feeling more satisfied and far more tolerant of each other's habits.

The following exercise is designed to assist you in the process of determining how you will approach dividing and performing the chores in your household.

Please list the current or future chores you do at home or will be doing as a couple. Indicate who does or will be doing each task: (S = self), with your partner (B = both) or by your partner (P = partner). Place a value from 1 (least attractive) to 10 (most attractive) next to each task.

Chore	**Performed by**	**Value**
Household		
Sweeping / vacuuming	______	____
Clean bathroom	______	____
Wash dishes	______	____
Load dishwasher	______	____
Empty dishwasher	______	____

Chore	Performed by	Value
Household (Continued)		
Clean kitchen (floor, countertops, appliances)	______	______
Cooking	______	______
Grocery shopping	______	______
Paying bills, reconciling accounts	______	______
Washing clothes	______	______
Fold and put away clothes	______	______
Other	______	______
Outdoors		
Landscape work	______	______
Lawn	______	______
Shrubs / garden	______	______
Clean-up	______	______
Other outdoor areas (deck/patio)	______	______
Other	______	______
Automobile		
Maintenance	______	______
Gas fill-up	______	______
Washing	______	______
Waxing	______	______
Parenting Tasks		
Feeding	______	______
Bathing	______	______
Chauffeuring	______	______
Babysitter arrangements (for a night out)	______	______
Food preparation	______	______
Diaper changes	______	______
Food shopping	______	______
Clothing shopping	______	______
Childcare arrangements (day-care and/or nanny)	______	______
Child's doctor/dentist appointments	______	______

Chore	Performed by	Value
Parenting Tasks (Continued)		
Child's social calendar (parties, play dates, etc.)	______	_____
Child's lessons (music, art, dance, etc.)	______	_____
Child's sports	______	_____
Child's school assignments	______	_____
Other	______	_____
Social calendar (for the couple)		
Initiating contacts	______	_____
Maintenance	______	_____
Holiday card preparation and mailing	______	_____
Taking care of birthday, graduation, etc., gifts	______	_____
Party preparations	______	_____
Religious activities (volunteer work, charitable giving)		
Mine	______	_____
Partner's	______	_____
Child's	______	_____
Other	______	_____

With this exercise in mind, how satisfactory is your current (or future) distribution of these tasks, in your opinion? ____

____

Do you believe this distribution will be viewed as satisfactory by your partner? Y/N ____

Please explain: ____

How do you think tasks could be more evenly, fairly or, perhaps effectively, distributed between the two of you in the future? ____

If you are proposing a change, what standard would you choose as a basis for the exchange (i.e., what guiding principle for allocating chores did you apply)?

_____ Time available _____ Skill level _____Strength

_____ Stamina _____ Preference _____ Gender appropriateness*

Share and Share Alike (Or Share, and Share Differently?)

"Sharing is sometimes more demanding than giving." — Mary Catherine Bateson

Okay, it's time to talk about sharing.

Despite its place in the top ten "lessons to learn" in any kindergarten curriculum, sharing can be a tough issue for couples. And when it comes to sharing, don't expect consistency from your partner (or even, for that matter, from yourself).

People are very idiosyncratic in the way they feel about sharing: which things they're happy to share, which they're not. The willingness to share also varies a fair amount according to a person's mood, the setting, and a host of other variables.

There's an endless list of what kinds of things we'll gladly share: advice (always), money, food, clothing, closet space. For most people a similarly long list covers what we are *not* willing to share: toothbrushes, towels, food, drinking glasses, etc. For others the list is fairly short.

We don't have to attribute this to selfishness or bad manners. Remember, we are all the products of different homes and different histories and, thus, we have different expectations. For some people, sharing certain things can seem too intimate or invasive, or may be seen as bad hygiene. Others just have a need to have their things kept in a certain way or in certain places and don't like having other people use their things.

TIM AND BECCA

In Tim's idealized vision of marriage, sharing almost everything was an important element. Becca had the same notion. Unfortunately, they didn't share the same view of what constituted appropriate sharing. Tim was annoyed when the tuna salad he'd made to last the rest of the week suddenly vanished into one of Becca's sandwiches. He was also peeved when the magazine he'd been reading was no longer where he had placed it, especially if his bookmark had been moved.

Tim knew that these were minor annoyances. But he still felt uncomfortable and a bit disrespected by Becca's disregard of his feelings. He also knew that he must be doing things that annoyed Becca and that there must be things she was annoyed about. However, he didn't hear a word or see any signs of this.

On the suggestion of his therapist, Tim went about resolving his discomfort in a rather uncharacteristic way for him. He took notes. He wrote down what was troubling him and then examined his list. The list wasn't that long and even to himself it seemed embarrassing. "Stupid and petty," is how he put it. He thought carefully about his complaints and decided that it was well past time for him to "grow up". He recognized that if Becca could put up with him and his foibles, he surely could do the same for her.

Are there items that you consider yours alone that you don't like to share with anyone (e.g., toothbrush, hairbrush and comb, razors, towels and washcloths, memorabilia/keepsakes, food/drink, etc.)? ____

How do you feel about your mate's desires and behaviors regarding sharing possessions, etc.?
____

Do you foresee any problems in this area? Y/N ___ If so, how do you think you can resolve your differences? ____
____
____

Communicating Thoughts and Feelings

"To effectively communicate, we must realize that we are all different in the way we perceive the world, and use this understanding as a guide to our communication with others." — Anthony Robbins

Expressing Affection

Do you know the joke about the old married couple sitting on a porch? The husband turns to the wife and says, "You know, Susan, we've been together for 50 years. And sometimes my feelings for you have been so deep and so strong that it's all I've been able to do to keep from telling you I love you."

The way we feel about both giving and receiving affection is an essential element in any intimate relationship. How much, and in which ways, different individuals are inclined to and willing to give and receive affection can vary a great deal.

This is not only a question of quantity but also quality, and personal style. The proper setting for the expression of affection, the tone used—light and bantering, serious and respectful, or not at all (as in the joke above!) all of these things can matter to a couple.

This section presents the opportunity for you to consider what pleases you, and to convey your thoughts about this matter to your partner. The variety of ways of expressing affection is boundless. For many couples it is conveyed in tender words, terms of endearment, pet names, or baby talk. For others, affection is communicated by actions: by doing special favors, giving thoughtful gifts, or finding other ways to please one's partner. For still others, an exchange of glances or a gentle touch can speak volumes. You are encouraged to explore and expand the ways that each of you prefers to express yourself affectionately. As in other areas, there's a fine balance between trying to please your partner in the way you know is agreeable to them and being allowed to just be yourself. There is no magic formula for where the give and take should begin and end. Ideally, you will meet somewhere in the middle—time and time again.

ANNA AND BRUCE

Anna was confused. Bruce repeatedly told her he loved her and was eager—both in private and in public—to hug her, touch her, kiss her. Anna, nonetheless questioned his sincerity. Bruce simply fell short of what Anna wanted: a man who would act in a way that she felt was consistent with his words and touch. By "acting," Anna meant doing things for her: picking up her dry cleaning, buying her special items, doing additional chores, etc. These acts, to Anna, defined love. Just words and touch fell short of the mark.

Anna tried very hard to convey this to Bruce. She tried to show him how to do this, through her own very thoughtful acts, because she loved him and also because she was trying to instruct him in what she needed to feel loved.

Bruce, quite honestly just didn't get it. He was sure he was spot on with what it took to reassure Anna of his devotion to her. He thought this because those touches, kisses, caresses, and tender words were exactly what he was so eager to receive from Anna.

Bruce and Anna were a couple that seemed to be making a science of not understanding each other's needs. Their premarital counselor picked up on this communication gap and referred them to a psychologist. After only a handful of meetings, the couple left with a set of skills that added to their improved understanding of themselves and each other.

How do you wish to be shown affection by your partner? Indicate with a check mark and explain.

__Words ______________________________

__Touch ______________________________

__Gifts ______________________________

__Actions ______________________________

__Other ______________________________

How do you like to show affection for your partner? Indicate with a check mark and explain.

__Words ______________________________

__Touch ______________________________

__Gifts ______________________________

__Actions ______________________________

__Other ______________________________

On the following scale, describe how important it is to you that your partner express affection in the way you prefer.

Not very important — Very important

1 2 3 4 5 6 7 8 9 10

Are there ways you would prefer that your partner *not* show you affection? Y/N ____

If yes, please explain. ______________________________

If there are ways your partner would prefer *not* to be shown affection, how would you like this to be explained to you? ______________________________

What are the specific times, ways, and places you especially desire to be shown affection?________

____

What are the specific times, ways, and places you especially prefer to express affection to your partner? ____

____

Describe the way your parents (or other important role models) expressed affection for each other. ____

Do you hope that your relationship with your partner will be similar to your parents' relationship in this regard? Or perhaps opposite? Or somewhere in-between? ______________________________

____

Arguments (Or, Preferably, Disagreements)

To keep your marriage brimming,
With love in the loving cup,
Whenever you're wrong, admit it;
Whenever you're right, shut up. — Ogden Nash

Oh, would that yours might be a relationship free of disagreements!

But on second thought, maybe that wouldn't be so terrific after all. A marriage without arguments is not necessarily a perfect marriage. In any relationship, no matter how loving and respectful, two autonomous adults are going to disagree about things from time to time; but they need not be disagreeable with each other when this occurs.

With all due respect to the sentiment playfully expressed above by Ogden Nash, there's another apt quote on this topic. Ben Shahn, a twentieth century writer and artist, observed, "You have not converted a man because you have silenced him." If one of you is being badgered or intimidated into silence, nothing has been done to advance the worthy goals of airing your differences, respectfully listening to each other, and resolving issues that need to be resolved. ***There needs to be room for some disagreement in any healthy relationship.***

It's not the fact that couples argue, but ***how*** they argue, that gives psychologists a window into the health of a relationship. You do not want to have to lose yourself in order to strengthen your bond to your partner. Remember, the person your fiancé fell in love with was not a clone of himself or herself, but a three-dimensional, evolving person who is virtually certain to *not* always agree with him or her on everything all of the time.

The first key to being able to engage in healthy disagreement is maintaining a foundation of fundamental respect for your partner, even when you don't agree about something.

The second essential ingredient is humility. "Yes, I realize that I could be wrong. Therefore, I want to better understand where my partner is coming from."

The ultimate goal is that each of you is capable of seeing the other's point of view and having empathy for his or her feelings.

There will inevitably be times when your feelings will be hurt by your partner, by the things they do or say, or by the things they fail to do or say. When you feel wronged, you will have to find a way to forgive.

For some, this is no mean feat. Some of us, when injured, feel it necessary to strike back. Others shut down emotionally. Still others seek distractions. Some of these distractions are harmless or even therapeutic (a walk, a workout); others are harmful (drugs, alcohol, retaliatory sexual activity, or withholding).

The following questions attempt to tease out your feelings about arguments: how to get over the injury and how to forgive each other and repair your relationship.

RICK AND PAM

Do you have to always be right? Rick did. This even extended to when he was wrong. Pam was no pushover. However she felt that the heat generated by her frequent disagreements with Rick was just too depleting. Even when she was certain that water boils at 100°C, and he insisted that it did not, she decided it wasn't worth the trouble to disagree with him.

This way of communicating—or rather, of failing to communicate effectively with each other—began to corrode their relationship. Pam became quieter, and Rick became bewildered. She knew this wasn't the way to proceed in a relationship. Yet she didn't know how to address this problem with Rick. She didn't want to provoke yet another argument.

Their minister caught a glimpse of Rick's argumentative style when they participated in his marriage preparation course. He began to make inquiries. He found out that Rick had been bullied by both his dad and his older brother. Rick had learned to see losing an argument as a threat to his manhood.

Their minister suggested that Rick practice catching himself needing to be right—not just preferring to be—whether with Pam or with others. The minister also suggested to Pam that she learn to speak up gently but not be silenced when she felt a growing tension between herself and Rick. They are working on this issue. It's been painful for both of them but productive, and it actually improved their relationship.

These first questions address how you and your fiancé *currently* deal with disagreement.

What are the topics over which you typically disagree? ____________________

____

What topics do you consider off-limits (e.g., my kids, my parents, my religious practices or beliefs, politics)? This can include areas where even if your partner is "right" you are not open to discussing things, since it is an emotional, not a rational, issue for you. ____________________

____

How would you describe a fair fight? ____________________

____

What seems to cause things to get out of hand between you and your partner? ____________________

____

What do you consider unfair fighting? ____________________

How would you describe the way you act when you are arguing with your partner?

☐ Loud ☐ Silent ☐ Sulking ☐ Sarcastic ☐ Sweet ☐ Calm

☐ Profane ☐ Logical ☐ Insulting ☐ Understanding ☐ Assertive ☐ Respectful

Other ____________________

How would you describe the way your partner acts during arguments?

☐ Loud ☐ Silent ☐ Sulking ☐ Sarcastic ☐ Sweet ☐ Calm

☐ Profane ☐ Logical ☐ Insulting ☐ Understanding ☐ Assertive ☐ Respectful

Other ___________________

What changes do you propose for each of you?

Myself ____

My partner ____

How are your arguments usually resolved?

☐ Reason ☐ Emotion (raised voices, tears) ☐ Coin flip

☐ They are left unresolved ☐ We agree to disagree

☐ Mediation/outside intervention (by whom?) _________________________________

How do you handle the aftermath of a fight? ___________________________________

____

How important are apologies to you? ____

How important are apologies to your partner? ___________________________________

In what form are these apologies?

☐ Written ☐ By self ☐ By fiancé

☐ Spoken ☐ By self ☐ By fiancé

☐ Something tangible (e.g., flowers, gift) ______________ ☐ By self ☐ By fiancé

☐ Other ______________ ☐ By self ☐ By fiancé

How long do you keep a grudge? _________________________________

What usually makes you feel better about your partner after an argument? _____________

____

And if that doesn't work? ____

How do you two usually make up?

☐ I take the initiative and apologize.

☐ My fiancé takes the initiative and apologizes.

☐ We let things cool down. (For how long?) ___________________

☐ We pretend it never happened.

☐ We celebrate by

☐ Going out to eat, dance, etc.

☐ Making love

☐ Buying something for each other

☐ Other ____________________

Now please look at the following questions, and this time, describe how you *wish* to engage in and resolve future disagreements.

What are the topics over which you feel it's important to voice your differing opinions?__________

____

What topics should be considered off-limits? ______________________________________

____

How would you describe a fair fight? ____

____

What might cause a fair fight to escalate into something not so fair? ____________________

____

What would you consider unfair fighting? ____

____

How would you *like* to act during an argument?

☐ Loud ☐ Silent ☐ Sulking ☐ Sarcastic ☐ Sweet ☐ Calm

☐ Profane ☐ Logical ☐ Insulting ☐ Understanding ☐ Assertive ☐ Respectful

Other ___________________

How do you *wish* your partner would act during an argument?

☐ Loud ☐ Silent ☐ Sulking ☐ Sarcastic ☐ Sweet ☐ Calm

☐ Profane ☐ Logical ☐ Insulting ☐ Understanding ☐ Assertive ☐ Respectful

Other ___________________

Ideally, how would you wish your future arguments to be resolved?

☐ Reason ☐ Emotion ☐ Coin flip ☐ Remain unresolved ☐ Agree to disagree

☐ Mediation/outside intervention (by whom?) ______________________________________

Ideally, how would you *like* to handle the aftermath of a fight? ________________________

____

How important would you want apologies to be for you, ideally? _______________________

____

In what form would you prefer these apologies be delivered?

☐ Written ☐ By self ☐ By fiancé

☐ Spoken ☐ By self ☐ By fiancé

☐ Something tangible (e.g. flowers, gift) ☐ By self ☐ By fiancé

☐ Other ___________________ ☐ By self ☐ By fiancé

Ideally, how long would you keep a grudge? _______________________________________

How would you prefer to come around after an argument?

___Talk with my partner ___Joke with my partner ___Act contrite ___Beg ____Cajole

___Have my need for silence respected ___Change the subject __Other ______________

And if that didn't work? ____

____

Ideally, how would you two make up?

- ☐ I would take the initiative and apologize.
- ☐ My fiancé would take the initiative and apologize.
- ☐ We would let things cool down. (How long?)______________________
- ☐ Pretend it never happened.
- ☐ Celebrate by
  - ☐ Going out to eat, dance, etc.
  - ☐ Making love
  - ☐ Buying something
  - ☐ Other ________________

NOTE: Too many couples allow silence, or "agreeing to disagree," be the default outcome of their disagreements. When this happens, there may be important areas of discord left unresolved. Failing to address important issues can lay a faulty foundation that can lead to serious problems in a relationship.

In such cases, silence is *not* "the better part of valor." It can instead be the hidden enemy from within. Please consider courageously addressing substantive issues so that they don't grow from small and tender wounds into cancerous growths.

"How Do You Like My Hair?" (Compliments/Criticism)

"I think a compliment ought always to precede a complaint, where one is possible, because it softens resentment and insures for the complaint a courteous and gentle reception." — Mark Twain

The way we go about giving and receiving compliments and criticism is very, very important to many people. Some people seem to just have a knack for knowing how to express criticism without making the person being criticized feel they are under attack. For others, it is an acquired skill. Also, some people are very easily insulted, and others let criticism roll off their backs much more easily.

A willingness to teach your partner how you like to be complimented, as well as what would make being criticized easier to accept, is important for every couple. Just because you may have had experience with other relationships, please remember that each person and relationship is unique, and everyone has their own idiosyncratic preferences. This is a case in which one style does not fit all!

VICKI AND JASON

Vicki seemed to never respond favorably to Jason's compliments. She'd ignore them, frown, or actually belittle them. Not surprisingly, Jason found this very painful. He worried that Vicki was either taking his comments for granted, or doubting their sincerity. He thought she was devaluing them, that his compliments were not as worthwhile as those she heard from someone else. This, for Jason, became a source of growing irritation. He didn't raise the issue with Vicki, but it was simmering in him, making him feel really troubled, especially when he found himself wanting to say something complimentary and then purposely holding himself back.

When Jason finally raised this issue with Vicki she was able, through tears, to reveal to him that her father would, as she recalled, compliment her mother on virtually everything she did. It even embarrassed the young Vicki how often this parental interchange occurred, especially in public. Vicki subsequently learned that her father had been carrying on a long-standing affair with another woman. Vicki came to see her father's compliments to her mother as an outrageous sham, and when Jason complimented her it reminded her of her father's betrayal. The couple talked about this at length. Vicki resolved to hear Jason's voice as his own, to receive his compliments as genuine, and to stop viewing all men as duplicitous. It was a breakthrough in their relationship and also a way for Vicki to begin to overcome the pain of her father's betrayal of her mother.

Giving and Receiving Compliments

How do you feel about receiving compliments, in general? (Check as many as apply.)

____ It's important ____ It's unimportant ____ I'm embarrassed ____ I'm pleased

____ I feel condescended to ____ Other ___________________

How do you feel about receiving compliments from your partner? ______________________

____

____

How do you feel about giving compliments to your partner? ______________________

____

____

Unimportant									Very important
1	2	3	4	5	6	7	8	9	10

Using the scale above:

Please indicate the importance you place on *giving* compliments to your partner ____________

Please indicate the importance you place on *receiving* compliments from your partner__________

Unskillful									Very skillful
1	2	3	4	5	6	7	8	9	10

Using the scale above:

How would you rate your partner's ability to give compliments? _____

How would you rate yourself? _____

Giving and Receiving Criticism

How do you feel about receiving criticism, in general? (Check as many as apply.)

____ annoyed ____ neutral ____ appreciative ____ embarrassed ___ Other ______

How do you feel about receiving criticism from your *partner*?

____ annoyed ____ neutral ____appreciative ____ unappreciated

____ embarrassed ____ loved ____ unloved ____ Other _________

How do you distinguish between constructive and destructive criticism?__________________

____

Very sensitive									Comfortable
1	2	3	4	5	6	7	8	9	10

Using the scale above:

How would you rate your level of comfort with being criticized by your partner? ____________

How would you rate your partner's level of comfort with being criticized by you? ____________

What rules do you wish to apply to the exchange of criticism between you and your partner?

____

What topics are off-limits (i.e., should not be criticized)?

For Self	For Partner
☐ Weight	☐
☐ Diet	☐
☐ Physical appearance	☐
☐ Intellect	☐
☐ Sense of Humor	☐
☐ Family	☐
☐ Children	☐
☐ Stepchildren	☐
☐ Parents	☐
☐ Siblings	☐
☐ Ethnic background	☐
☐ Religion	☐
☐ Neatness	☐
☐ Spending choices	☐
☐ Sexual performance	☐
☐ Interest in sex	☐
☐ Other__________	__________ ☐
☐ Other__________	__________ ☐
☐ Other__________	__________ ☐

If there are things about any of the above that really bother your partner, what could your partner do to let you know he/she needs to talk about it without hurting your feelings or causing an unpleasant argument? ____

____

Can You Take a Joke? (And Can Your Partner?)

"What a strange world this would be if we all had the same sense of humor." — Bern Williams

No one likes to be told they lack a sense of humor. But people differ a great deal in what they find humorous. This is particularly true if they, or a group they identify with, are frequently made the object of jokes.

The way we like to entertain others with our humor and the way we like to be entertained ourselves can be areas of great differences of opinion—and also quite revealing of some of our most important beliefs and character traits.

The questions below will give you an opportunity to think about your own sense of humor. Some of the things you discover about yourself may be beneficial to share with your partner. Remember, the better you understand each other and your lightning-rod areas of sensitivity, the better the chances that your relationship will be able to thrive over the long term, and that you'll be able to appreciate (or at least understand) each other's jokes and sense of humor, even if they are not identical.

JULIA AND DAN

For Julia, Dan's jokes and ribbing always felt less than funny, even from the onset of their courtship. As they grew closer, contrary to her expectations, Dan's "good-natured" gibes hurt all the more. Try as she might, Julia simply couldn't get used to Dan's ribbing, nor could she see it as simply being good-natured. To her, Dan's jokes seemed more like deliberate jabs than playful gibes. When she raised this issue with him more than once or twice, Dan retreated. He did, temporarily, stop the "funny" commentary; but he also fell silent a bit sullenly.

The couple talked with Dan's father, to whom both of them felt very close, about this matter. He tried to explain Dan's behavior as a "guy thing"... the way close friends and best friends could be almost vicious in their humorous needling of each other and their practical jokes. This explanation helped Julia a bit, but only temporarily.

The couple eventually found themselves in a psychologist's consultation room. There another take on Dan's humor was proposed. Perhaps there was a not-so-veiled message behind Dan's humor. Perhaps Dan could learn to be more direct in his requests for change from Julia and in his way of speaking his mind. This idea, for Dan, felt rather refreshing, even liberating. He hadn't ever really dared to trust his feelings and judgments to the extent that he could be open with Julia in this way. For Dan, this level of honest communication added to the strength of the bond between himself and Julia. He began to find ways to deal with her more directly, and she felt much more comfortable with his new style.

How would you describe your sense of humor?

___ dry ___ discriminating ___ very accepting ___ loud ___ sarcastic

___subtle ___ selective ___ profane ___ prudish _____ raunchy ___ other_______

How would you describe your partner's sense of humor?

___ dry ___ discriminating ___ very accepting ___ loud ___sarcastic

___ subtle ___ selective ___ profane ___ prudish _____ raunchy ___ other________

What do you find really funny? (movies/books/comedians/people you know, etc.) Alternatively, just describe the kind of things that tend to make you laugh. ______________________________

____

What *don't* you consider to be funny?______________________________________

____

Are there any particular kinds of humor that you find offensive? ___________________

If there were a specific aspect of your partner's sense of humor (e.g., teasing) that you could change, what would it be? ____

Using the scale below, how similar do you see your sense of humor to your partner's?

Not At All Similar — Very Similar

1 2 3 4 5 6 7 8 9 10

Is it important that your partner finds the same things funny that you do? Y/N ___

Please explain ____

If there are particular kinds of jokes that your *partner* tells that are offensive to you, how can you resolve this problem? ____

What about practical jokes? ____

If there are particular kinds of jokes that *you* tell that are offensive to your partner, how can you resolve this problem? ____

____

What about practical jokes? ____

Language: Watch What You Say!

"Whatever words we utter should be chosen with care for people will hear them and be influenced by them for good or ill." — Buddha

This is a ticklish topic which can be easily overlooked by couples—at least until it offends. The use of questionable language can reflect familial, cultural, gender, and other factors. Language can caress, offend, surprise, or arouse. Underestimating the power of words can be dangerous.

Language that is especially sexual, scatological, bigoted, or religious is loaded with the potential for misunderstandings between couples. It's better to consider and address any strong feelings you have about this matter before you get married than to believe that whatever you find offensive in your partner's way of speaking will just go away on its own.

PHIL AND AMELIA

When "Jew" became a verb and "watermelon man" a blunt code word Amelia used with increasing frequency, Phil found himself looking for an opportunity to tell her that he objected to her choice of words and the not-so-latent prejudices he feared they revealed. He tried to be more tolerant of Amelia's behavior, making allowances for her new work environment, where she claimed she had the cards stacked against her and felt that she was the victim of anti-female, anti-Hispanic prejudice. Nonetheless, as their relationship became exclusive and they talked about marriage, Phil grew increasingly uncomfortable. He knew that he couldn't bear such a verbal and attitudinal environment when, as he hoped, children would be a part of their lives. Phil also worried that Amelia would slip by making an insensitive remark in front of his friends or family, who emphatically didn't share her attitudes.

Phil felt good about raising this issue, but Amelia was hurt, annoyed, and probably embarrassed that he hadn't mentioned it earlier. Once the initial dust had settled, Amelia had to admit that she probably had allowed her frustration at work to cause her to make some inappropriate comments. Her negative and stereotyping comments stopped, and Phil and Amelia grew closer.

For partners who do not share the same first language, the following questions may be especially relevant.

Using the scale below:

How well do you understand what your partner tries to express to you verbally? ____________

How well does your partner understand what you try to express verbally? ________________

Do Not Understand									Understand Very Well
1	2	3	4	5	6	7	8	9	10

If there are significant differences in comprehension, how do you propose to address this issue? ______________________________

____

How do you feel about terms of endearment, special nicknames, or "baby talk" between partners? ______________________________

____

Do you have a nickname you wish to be called by? Y/N ___

Please specify both name and the setting in which it is appropriate. ______________

____

Do you have an aversion to being called by a certain name? Y/N ___

Please specify both name and the setting in which it is inappropriate. ______________

____

How do you feel about profanity (this includes insulting racial terms, sexual, and scatological terms)? ______________________________

Where/when if at all, do you find profanity appropriate? ______________________

____

Where/when is it not? ______________________________

What "trigger" words (e.g., sexual or scatological terms, racial/ethnic epithets) do you want your partner to avoid:

In your bedroom ______________________________

In your household ______________________________

Around your friends ______________________________

Around your family ______________________________

Around your children______________________________

Around anybody's children ______________________________

Are there any words that your partner should always avoid in your presence? ______________

____

Dreams and Goals, Expectations and Ideals

"Knowledge of what is does not open the door directly to what should be." — Albert Einstein

In the backs of our minds we all harbor a view of the way things "should" be: the way a career should unfold, the way and the rate at which children should develop, the way homes should be kept tidy, the way guests should be entertained, the way we should spend vacations or leisure time, etc.

But "should" is actually a very dangerous concept. Saying something *should* be a certain way implies that "I know how it's supposed to be (and perhaps you don't)." Far more useful, and much less aggressive, is the word "prefer," which suggests that there is room for variation and differences of opinion about all of these matters.

Within the context of marriage, the "shoulds" that you might be harboring in your mind can be powerful and potentially destructive. The more you talk with your partner about the way you each feel things "should" be, the more likely that you will be able to find constructive ways to bridge whatever gaps may exist between the two of you.

When it comes to your wedding, for example, by examining the source of your feelings about what "should" be, you may come to better understand why you have been so steadfastly insisting on the importance of having a night versus an afternoon wedding reception, a jazz quartet versus a rock band, or lavender rather than chartreuse bridesmaids' dresses. You may also understand why it is that the more you insist on having things your way, the more distant you feel from your fiancé, who might be beginning to feel like it is *your* wedding and not a special day for the *two* of you to share.

Planning for a wedding presents a good opportunity to practice the all-important art of compromise, probably the single most important quality required for successful marriages. So whenever you find yourselves "should-ing" each other, take a deep breath and ask yourselves what is more important: doing whatever it is "correctly"? Or pleasing each other and sharing a stake in the outcome?

I'm not going to tell you the answer to that question. I trust that you'll be able to decide for yourselves.

BLAKE AND BETSY

Blake and Betsy, like most couples, had set ideas about how they should live their lives. After all, they weren't teenagers anymore. Now in their early 30's, both of them felt that their judgment was sound and that the decisions they made, based on their judgment, were also sound. And, to a large extent, the couple agreed on most everything. This made for a lot of harmony and even deepened their sense that theirs was a union that was destined to be lasting and harmonious.

Imagine their surprise and dismay when they came to loggerheads over their bridal registry china pattern! Though, actually, the problem was a bit more complicated than that. It turns out that Blake's mother had set ideas that biased his choice, and Betsy (with a little help from her friends) strongly disagreed with that choice. The choices that set the couple's teeth on edge and led them to dig in their respective heels were fancy versus plain, practical versus stylish, fine china versus pottery.

It soon became apparent, through the good advice of the helpful bridal registry consultant, that the couple wasn't arguing about their preferences in chinaware: the argument really was about who was "right" in their selection. In other words, they were faced with a bad case of the "tyranny of shoulds." The couple's very blissful courtship, free of any serious clashes, hadn't given them the experience of working through a strong disagreement before. Nor did they seem to understand that what they were clashing over was actually a very benign and simple disagreement. The consultant pointed out that they were telling each other how they should feel instead of trying to understand each other's points of view. They also came to realize that their discord was being made worse by the outside pressures they were both experiencing.

Lo and behold, the registry consultant's wisdom took hold. Blake and Betsy chose a third pattern, totally different from either of the earlier selections, as a respectful compromise. This quite possibly provided a model for future resolutions of conflict, as well as the need for couples to set limits to the potentially unhelpful involvement of friends and family in such matters.

How would you describe the ideal relationship/marriage? ____________________

____

Where did you observe this ideal (e.g., parents, friends, books, movies)? ____________________

____

In reference to this "ideal," how would you describe your relationship with your partner?

____

In reference to this "ideal," how do you expect your marriage to develop in the future?

____

Do you believe that love inevitably will fade? Y/N ___ Please explain. ____________________

____

____

Do you believe that romance inevitably will fade? Y/N ___ Please explain. ____________________

____

How does one make a marriage thrive? ____

____

____

Is there a specific "script" you have in mind for how your marital lives will unfold (e.g., house in the suburbs, exciting careers, well-behaved children, etc.)? Y/N ___ Please elaborate. ______________

____

____

If your partner came up with a very different scenario in mind (living on a houseboat, taking time off from career paths, having children along while you travel, doing volunteer work in another country), how would you respond to a disruption of your script? _____________________________

____

____

How do you propose that the two of you reconcile these potential differences? ________________

____

____

Is Having Children an Important Part of Your Future Together?

"The soul is healed by being with children." English proverb

"I would have liked having children to some degree, but frankly I haven't got the time to take the kids to the goddamn ballgame." Albert Ellis

Some couples choose to marry primarily because they have decided to have children, so the question of whether or not to start a family is already settled. For other couples, there is less certainty about this question, at least in the mind of one or the other partner.

Most couples are savvy enough to know that the arrival of children in a family is a life-changing event, even more momentous than marrying. Children do not come with a guarantee; they are not exchangeable or refundable; and parents are not allowed to divorce their kids. So having children is a lifetime commitment. The responsibility outlasts fire, flood, other natural disasters, all manner of everyday crises, and yes, divorce, too. Therefore the question of whether to have children and how they are to be raised is an enormous one.

Your own experiences as a child will probably influence your decision about whether to have children yourself. And if you decide to have children, your own experiences as a child will also affect the way you choose to raise your children. (Whether you decide to do things more or less the way your parents did, *not* the way yours parents did, or some combination of the two.) The way your siblings, childhood friends, and possibly the way you have seen friends and relatives raise their children will also help inform the style of childrearing you develop.

As in every other aspect of your marriage, you should not expect that you and your partner will have identical ideas and opinions about childrearing. But perhaps in this area more than any other it is important to find ways to work together harmoniously for the good of the children and for the sake of the marriage, despite any differences you may have.

As you answer the questions that follow, you are encouraged to note how strongly they reflect your deepest beliefs about having children. It's important to be very honest so that your answers can help spur fruitful, productive discussions as they are matched against your partner's replies. The reconciliation of differences and the overlapping of similar answers will help you to move forward as you make decisions about this potentially major focus of your lives.

Reflecting on what you want as a future parent, as well as why you want it, can be useful in considering your own replies as well as in sharing them. Once you have thoroughly thought through this matter and talked it over with your partner, you may change your mind about some things. If so, good for you! That means the process is working!

If not, if you have been perfectly honest in your responses and your partner has too, and you see eye-to-eye about these matters, that's great too. You should have no rude awakenings later.

If there are significant areas of disagreement, this may be something you will want to explore with a counselor, member of the clergy, or trusted friends and relatives.

ARNOLD AND HELEN

Arnold believed he was doomed. Early trauma had rendered him infertile. He dreaded the day he'd have to disclose this to a woman with whom he was romantically involved. Arnold was not, by temperament, someone who would just blurt things out; in fact he tended to be quite reserved with personal information. Because of this, procrastination suited him just fine, particularly when he faced tough decisions or tasks.

Telling Helen, whom he had grown to love during an 18-month dating relationship, about his infertility became a larger and larger burden. Arnold felt like he was bearing the weight of the world on his shoulders, as he each day postponed the inevitable. He believed that upon hearing of his condition, Helen would want to end their relationship.

As the couple grew closer and Helen began to talk of marriage, Arnold became even more uneasy. He very much wanted to marry Helen and live out his life with her. But now he was facing the necessity of telling her his awful secret as well as disclosing that he had led her on, by failing to reveal this earlier. Finally, he screwed up his courage and told Helen everything. She, happily, took the news well. She was very happy to hear that Arnold wished to marry her, but she needed a little time to digest the news. Two days later they met and talked about what to do. Helen had indeed wanted her own biological children, but she loved Arnold enough to modify that dream. She asked if he would be open to various alternatives—further medical evaluation, the possibility of using a sperm donor so that she could experience pregnancy and have her biological child, and/or adoption. Arthur readily agreed to consider all of those options, and their wedding plans moved forward.

Do you wish to have children? Y/N ___ If yes, how many? ___

If more than one, how many years apart? _____

If you (or your partner) could not conceive, would you want to

- ___ Use fertility treatments
- ___ Hire a surrogate
  - ___ As a sperm donor
  - ___ As an egg donor
  - ___ To carry the fetus
- ___ Adopt a child
- ___ Become a foster parent
- ___ Focus on other areas of your lives

If you had an unplanned pregnancy, how would you wish, as a couple, to deal with this?________

____

If you could not agree about what to do about an unplanned pregnancy, how would you resolve your differences? ____

____

____

What will be the surname (last name) of your children? ______________________________

Do you have any strong feelings about the first name(s) of your children (e.g., naming children after deceased relatives, continuing the use of a family name followed by "Jr" or III, etc.) Y/N ___ Please explain ____

____

If so, how does your partner feel about this? ______________________________________

If there are disagreements about naming your children, how will you resolve them?____________

____

____

Defining Issues

Critical Incidents/Defining Moments

"But no matter how much planning you do, one tiny miscalculation, one moment of distraction, can end it all in an instant." — Jeannette Walls

Almost everyone has experienced a moment or a period of time that has made a huge difference in the way his or her life has unfolded (or sometimes just in the way we think about our lives).

Sometimes this event is of our own devising, sometimes we were swept along with larger events, sometimes we were mere witnesses to a public event (a political assassination, the moon landing, the explosion of the Challenger, the 9/11 attacks) or a private one (the death of a loved one).

These critical incidents and defining moments, and how we feel about them, make us who we are. It's good, and it can be helpful for your partner, to know what some of those moments have been in your life.

GARY AND BONNIE

Gary wept when he told Bonnie of the car crash in which his inebriated brother and his sister-in-law had died. This was a secret that he and his family had told virtually no one. Knowing about this tragic event helped Bonnie understand Gary's exceptional cautiousness on the road and his very strong, almost aggressive position when anyone they knew mixed drinking and driving. Gary's confiding in Bonnie helped both of them feel closer to each other and allowed Bonnie to be supportive and understanding of Gary in a way that was important to him.

In the space below describe one or more incidents that have helped shape you. Tell about the circumstances, the people involved, and the changes you subsequently underwent. What is it that you wish to convey to your partner about this event and how it affected you? Why is it so important to you, and what should your partner know about it, and its effect on you?

___

___

___

Do you know of any major events that have happened in your partner's life that may have similarly affected him or her? Y/N ___ (Note: If you don't know, now would probably be a good time to ask him or her this question!) Please explain: ____

____

____

____

Finances: For Richer, For Poorer

"Money is a nuisance! We'd all be much better off if it had never been invented. What does money matter as long as we are happy?" — Dr. Doolittle

Dr. Doolittle may have had a very good point. Money can be the dangerous "third rail" in a relationship.

Unfortunately, talking about money is necessary. But it is rarely a source of joyful dialogue. In fact, it is far too often the subject of heated, unpleasant discourse, occasionally leading to slammed doors or, at least, closed minds.

Why is this so?

Well, for starters, money is both limited and valuable. The amount of money in a household can mean the difference between being comfortable and secure or anxious and worried, and sometimes even physically uncomfortable.

Because it is limited, decisions frequently have to be made about which of several desirable things is more important. All of this can quite naturally lead to contention of one degree or another when it comes to making financial decisions. Decisions about money can magnify and come to symbolize a couple's power struggles, resentments, and even sex role* stereotyping.

One might think that for couples with enormous wealth, such issues would not be a problem; unfortunately, having "a great deal of money" is not so easy to arrange for most people. (And even those who do have lots of money do not always succeed in not thinking about it.)

Yes, believe it or not, even the wealthy wrestle with financial issues. Whether the money should be spent on luxury goods, services and travel, or philanthropy; whether it should be saved for the future, or for the children. These and other such choices can pose potential problems for any couple, no matter how rich or poor.

Choices about how financial resources should be spent reflect important personal values. Eventually you will need to find a way to form habits and priorities as a couple. These values will come from each of your own personal histories, the lessons you learned from your parents, your ethnic, ethical, educational, communal, and cultural biases, etc.

How much time will you devote to the accumulation of wealth versus leisure time pursuits? Such choices almost invariably arise for couples about both macro issues (job and career decisions, major purchases such as a home, public vs. private schooling) and micro issues (which restaurant to go to, what price entrée is within the budget, whether to go to a matinee or an evening performance, whether to use brand or generic drugs, etc.).

It's a good idea for couples-to-be to think about their individual spending habits, their capacity to make compromises, their ability to respect individual differences, and their ability to establish workable and flexible ground rules for how money will be spent in the household they will be creating together. The questions in this section will help you do that.

JERRY AND CHARLENE

Jerry had never been able to get a handle on his personal finances. Whatever he earned (and it was easily into the six figures), it quickly was spent. Although Jerry had an MBA, it didn't make him any more adept at reining in his appetite for expensive living. He also had problems tracking his expenses; he often exceeded his "plastic" limit, and incurred interest and penalties regularly.

Charlene was very much the opposite. She earned half what Jerry did but monitored her expenses closely. She kept a running balance on her checking account, always paid her bills promptly, and never risked incurring an interest charge on her one and only credit card.

Of course this didn't bode well for their marriage. Fortunately, Jerry and Charlene were able to discuss their differences before the wedding. They agreed to have three sets of accounts: "his," "hers," and "ours." They were to contribute, by percentage of salary, to the "ours" account for joint expenses. Jerry also agreed to keep to a budget for the "his" account, developed a payment plan to pay down his credit card debt, and promised not to use his old cards. He also opened a new credit card account with a low limit, which the couple jointly monitored.

Will this arrangement ensure that this couple will have no future financial disagreements? Probably not. But addressing the issue proactively certainly gives them a better head start than they would have had if they had failed to discuss it.

Using the scale below,

Poor									Wealthy
1	2	3	4	5	6	7	8	9	10

How would you describe the finances of your family of origin? ______

How would you describe the finances of your partner's family of origin? ______

Using the scale below,

Miser									Spendthrift
1	2	3	4	5	6	7	8	9	10

How would you describe your current spending habits? _______

How would you like to handle your spending in the future? ______

Using the same scale, how would you describe your partner's spending habits? _______

What would you like your partner's spending habits to be in the future? _______

When there are differences of opinion between you, whose opinion should prevail in your household?

___ Husband* ___ Whomever earns the most

___ Wife* ___ Whomever commands more assets (e.g. trust fund, wealthier parents, etc.)

___ The thriftiest option ___ Other, please specify ________________

___ Whomever feels the more strongly

Where there are currently differences of opinion, how do you hope to reconcile these differences?____

Using the checklist below, whose financial habits and inclinations do you think should prevail in your household?

	Me	Partner	To Be Determined
Everyday household items	☐	☐	☐
Big-ticket items (major appliances, etc.)	☐	☐	☐
Leisure activities	☐	☐	☐
Children's everyday expenses	☐	☐	☐
Big-ticket items for children (school, camp, etc.)	☐	☐	☐
Gifts	☐	☐	☐
Charitable giving (philanthropy)	☐	☐	☐
Other ___________________	☐	☐	☐
Other ___________________	☐	☐	☐
Other ___________________	☐	☐	☐

Please elaborate: ____

How do you want you and your partner to join assets/debts accumulated *prior to* the marriage?

☐ Everything held jointly

☐ Everything kept separate

☐ Other. Please explain ____

How do you think you and your partner should handle your *future* finances, both assets and debts?

☐ Everything held jointly

☐ Everything kept separate

☐ Other. Please explain ____

Do you anticipate a difference of opinion? Y/N ___ How do you propose to resolve this? ________

____

If there were to be a divorce, how would you divide your assets and debts? __________________

____

Will there be a prenuptial agreement regarding assets and debts held prior to your marriage? Y/N ___

How do you feel about this? ____

____

Would you like there to be a *postnuptial* agreement about assets obtained and debts incurred following your wedding? Y/N ___ Please explain ______________________________

As a couple, how do you wish to divide/control

Assets *earned* in the future? ______________________________

Assets *inherited* in the future? ______________________________

Debts incurred in the future (e.g., education loans, gambling debts, costs incurred for sick or dependent relatives)? ______________________________

Using the scale below, how much emphasis do you wish to place on savings?

Very Little Very Much

1 2 3 4 5 6 7 8 9 10

Using the scale below, how much emphasis do you wish your partner to place on savings?

Very Little Very Much

1 2 3 4 5 6 7 8 9 10

If there are children, who do you think should, or will, pay for their education?

College: Parents _____% Child _____% (loans) Grandparents/Relatives _____%

Post-college: Parents _____% Child _____% (loans) Grandparents/Relatives _____%

Will you two observe a budget? Y/N ___ If yes, how will this budget be established?____________

____

____

Do you wish to have separate discretionary accounts that you can use without consulting your partner? Y/N ___ Please explain ______________________________

How much would you like to be placed in these accounts? $_______/month or year

How often should this amount be replenished? ______________________________

____

If "yes," how much do you think is an appropriate ceiling for purchases made before you would consult with your partner? $_________

What rules should apply to you (type of purchase, for whom, etc.) for these expenditures?_______

____

What rules do you wish to apply to your partner's expenditures in these areas? _______________

____

How will you decide how much is an appropriate level for gift-giving? _____________________

____

How will you decide how much is an appropriate level for charitable giving? ________________

____

How will you decide if there is to be a ceiling above which you will have to consult with each other when spending money? ______________________________

How would you define financial security? ______________________________

____

How do you define wealth? ______________________________

____

How much money in reserve is "enough" for you to have a sense of security? ______________

____

How much money in reserve do you think your partner would see as "enough" in order to have a sense of security? ______________________________

Do you have any specific or general concerns about money, or how it will be handled in your household, that have not been covered in the questions above? If so, please explain them here: ______________

____

____

Independence/Dependence

"A long marriage is two people trying to dance a duet and two solos at the same time." — Anne Taylor Fleming

There is a wide variation in how much independence individuals need or desire in order to feel happy. How many of your day-to-day activities do you expect to engage in together in your free time? This question deserves your consideration now, and should also be periodically revisited in the future, so that you have the freedom to grow as individuals and as a couple.

Some couples are happily joined at the hip, and like to do most things together. They spend as much time as they can with each other. Other couples find constant "togetherness" stifling; these couples prefer to engage in many, maybe even most, of their activities separately, occasionally sharing some of the things that they like to do together.

Of course your preferences in this regard need not be permanent. People grow and change, decisions are revisited, couples go through various stages of life. Once again, there is no correct or magic formula for what works. What's important is that the way you handle this matter is supportive to each of you as individuals and to your relationship as a couple.

BARBARA AND BOB

Though they'd been seeing each other for over two years and had been engaged for ten months, Barbara took Bob's choice of a birthday present very hard. He wanted a day to himself! Of course Barbara knew that Bob was not exactly a people person. He often enjoyed alone time-whether it was hiking alone or going by himself to the movies. Still, one only has one birthday per year, and Bob was choosing to spend it without her.

Barbara knew her pain wouldn't easily subside. She also knew that she'd have to talk with Bob about the choice he had made, since to her it felt like a very important issue that was coming between them. Bob's response was, "Why does this have to be about you?" He felt very good about stating his needs and holding firm. But Barbara saw this as a danger sign and insisted that they enter into premarital counseling.

It turns out that Barbara had had no idea how differently she and Bob viewed the idealized ratio between alone time and together time. The more they spoke about this issue, the more the pieces began to fall into place. Bob was *choosing* to be away from Barbara, when she mistakenly thought he simply had obligations that prevented their being together. It turned out that many times his "having to do chores around my apartment" and "cleaning up from the week's work" was actually a need to stake out alone time for himself. Furthermore, in something of a reversal of a prior understanding, he adamantly did not want to move in with Barbara before their wedding.

> Therapy provided Bob and Barbara with a way of raising and discussing their different perspectives on what it meant to be a couple. Eventually, they decided to put their marital plans on hold while continuing to date each other. However, they also acknowledged to each other that theirs might not be an enduring relationship, since neither of them was willing to make the compromises suggested by their therapist.

Using the scale below, how much free time do you believe the ideal couple would choose to be together?

All the Time									Almost Never
1	2	3	4	5	6	7	8	9	10

Using the scale above, at present, how much of your free time do you spend with your partner?___

Using the scale above, how much of your free time do you expect to spend with your partner once you are married, or living together?___

Using the scale above, how do you think your partner would respond to this question? _________

Using the scale above, how would you like your partner to respond? ___

If your partner were to choose a very different number than the one you have chosen on this scale, how do you think you could reconcile your differences of opinion? ________________________

____

If your partner chooses to seek alone time at a time when you want to be with him or her, how would you wish to be told? ____

____

If you would like to be able to spend more alone time and your partner were to object, how would you feel about that? How could you resolve such a difference? ________________________

____

Parental Legacies and Lessons

"The highest form of wisdom is kindness." — Talmudic saying

Becoming parents is often the biggest change a couple experiences, especially in the early years of their relationship. The parenting you received and/or observed (e.g., by parents of friends or relatives) will provide a model for you as you go about fulfilling your own role as parent or stepparent.

Think about the other parenting lessons you've learned. Some of them are obvious and very explicit ("Share the credit for achievements," "Wvork hard in school."). Others are a little more vague but just as important ("Be humble," "Put your best foot forward," "Be kind."). Some lessons are "don'ts" ("Don't show off."), while others are "do's" ("Leave a good tip."). Some lessons are conditional ("It's okay to wear raggedy clothes, but only at home."). Others are unconditional ("Never lie.").

These are just a few examples of the many ways your parents may have influenced you. Hopefully, replying to the questions in this section will inspire you to consider some of the things you were taught by your parents or other role models and become more aware of the principles, values, and examples that have shaped you, so that you can better understand yourself and explain yourself to your fiancé.

BARRY AND DIANA

Barry felt he had learned this lesson well: "Never hit." He was intensely ashamed that his father had struck his mother, not often, but often enough. Not only did he hear it, but he once witnessed it, and that moment was branded into his brain. For a long time, the residue of this nightmarish scene kept Barry from even considering himself capable of having a serious relationship.

Ironically, aside from this matter, Barry thought the world of his father, and they were very close. You could almost say that Barry idolized his father, which created a great deal of dissonance for him. If someone he loved and admired so much could strike out and hit someone, then it was conceivable that he, too, could do such an appalling thing.

Then Barry met and fell in love with Diana. When they were set to wed, Barry knew he'd have to eventually tell Diana about his family legacy of shame, but he was filled with fear. What would Diana think of his father when she knew? Could she ever completely trust Barry to control himself? He was also filled with shame. He did not want Diana to reflect on this one aspect of his family to the exclusion of so much else about them.

Finally Barry talked about this sorry side of his history with Diana. Barry felt she took it very well. She seemed much more concerned about Barry and the trauma he had suffered than worried that he'd be prone to behave in the way his dad had done.

What message, set of values, or rules to guide you has your father provided you with? What legacy, lessons, or core belief system have you learned from him? ______________________________

What message, set of values, or rules to guide you has your mother provided you with? What legacy, lessons, or core belief system have you learned from her?

What message, set of values, or rules to guide you have your grandfathers provided you with? What legacy, lessons, or core belief system have you learned from them?

What message, set of values, or rules to guide you have your grandmothers provided you with? What legacy, lessons, or core belief system have you learned from them?

Who are the other significant people who have contributed substantially to make you the person you are and shaped your core beliefs about yourself, the future, and your place in it?

Person | Legacy/Core Beliefs

:

:

:

:

Which of the values that you learned from your parents, grandparents, or others do you definitely want to pass on to your children? Please explain

Are there any things you learned from your parents that you *do not* want to teach, or pass on, to your children?

Politics

"Let us, on both sides, lay aside our arrogance. Let us not, on either side, claim that we have already discovered the truth." — St. Augustine

Republican/Democrat ... Liberal/Conservative ... Libertarian/Independent.

For some people, these labels are extremely important. For others, not so much. Political identification can affect our choices regarding friendships, neighborhoods, and religious communities.

Or do our choices of friends, neighborhoods, and religious communities affect our politics? Probably, it's a little of each.

How strongly you hold to your political/philosophical identities can be a useful subject to explore with your partner. Knowing how important these issues are to each of you and how you feel about them is a good thing to discuss at this point in your relationship. There have been some very famous (and successful) marriages between people who are both quite political but have very different political beliefs. Political differences don't have to be an obstacle to a loving relationship. But it's good to know before you get married how you will handle your differences of opinion.

EMMA AND JUAN

It's a bit of a mystery how couples with vastly different political leanings get together but this was not such a mystery to Emma and Juan. The mystery for them was how to stay together. Their battles around politics were famous among their friends. There was no pottery thrown, nor were invectives tossed, but the volume of their voices would rise, and extreme statements (often not even believed by the speaker) were asserted. Yet, at the end of the day, Emma and Juan would make up and were able to put aside their battles because they were deeply in love and strongly attracted to each other. In fact, they both conceded, their pleasures in lovemaking seemed directly proportional to the volatility of their last political scrap.

The reason the couple arranged for a pre-wedding tune-up was because both their friends and family were very distressed by their pyrotechnics. They feared that the couple would come to an unhappy end, given the level of acrimony in their political debates. After reviewing some cautionary rules about how to handle disagreements respectfully, Emma and Juan were sent on their way (See "Arguments" for more on this.)

Political arguments may be no more ominous than arguments about finances, relatives, children, or religion. Emma and Juan may actually have a more auspicious trajectory for their marriage than many, because at least their disagreements were out in the open. Neither of them had any secret agendas. Neither had plans to become a flaming liberal nor an arch conservative, at least for the foreseeable future. And certainly any changes they made would not be made solely by the force of their spouse's persuasion.

Using the scale below, indicate how important political events are to you.___

Unimportant									Very important
1	2	3	4	5	6	7	8	9	10

Using this same scale, indicate how important national current events are to you. ___

Using this same scale, indicate how important international current events are to you.___

With which political parties or organized movements do you choose to affiliate (e.g., Libertarian, Democratic, Republican, Christian Evangelical, Zionism, Abortion Rights, Tea Party, etc.)? ______

____

Are you a "single issue" voter (i.e., the position of the candidate on a particular issue is likely to be the sole determinant for how you will vote)? Y/N ___

If yes, which issue are you most concerned about? ______________________

____

Using the scale above:

How important to you is it that your partner shares your political affiliation(s)? _______ Please explain. ______________________________

____

How important to you is it that your partner shares your political position(s)? _______ Please explain. ______________________________

____

How important is it that your friends, family, and in-laws share your political affiliation(s)? _______ Please explain. ______________________________

____

How important is it (using the scale above) that your friends, family, and in-laws share your political position(s)? ______ Please explain ______________________________

____

If you and your partner have very different opinions about politics, current national and political affairs, etc., how will you handle your differences? ______________________

____

If at some point in the *future* you and your partner developed very different opinions about politics, how do you think you would handle your differences? ______________________

____

Quirks (Idiosyncratic Likes/Dislikes/Fears/Prejudices)

"A great marriage is not when the 'perfect couple' lives together. It is when an imperfect couple learns to enjoy their differences." — Dave Meurer

There is an essential life skill that psychologists call "discrimination," which means the use of good judgment, discretion, and generalization to assist us in making choices. Discrimination helps us make appropriate choices when faced with challenging circumstances (e.g., choosing to walk on a broad, well-lit street versus a narrow, darkened alley when alone at night in a strange neighborhood; adhering to speed limits, especially in hazardous driving conditions or in unfamiliar areas; choosing not to gamble, especially when money is tight and the temptation is great).

Most people use discrimination to make good choices in many areas of their lives; some people could do a better job of it in at least some areas. Some of our fears and prejudices may be irrational or even destructive. As you record your answers to the following questions, use your replies as a way to learn more about yourself, and share your replies with your partner. Your replies need not be exhaustive; even short answers to these questions can be very revealing and helpful in getting to know who you are.

In the process of thinking about this, you may want to re-evaluate some of your beliefs. Your partner can share his/her list with you, too, and together you can evaluate the wisdom or folly behind some of your quirks.

BENNETT AND MANDY

Bennett's quirk was very difficult to disclose to Mandy. It had not come up in the many months they knew each other. He felt embarrassed and humiliated by his morbid fear of rodents, especially mice and rats. Bennett had even dropped his choice of psychology as a major in college because of a mandatory laboratory course that required handling laboratory rats.

Of course, Bennett knew that others shared this aversion. But, he felt it was very unmanly to have such a fear, and he feared that it would make him the subject of much ridicule. Once, when he was walking in a darkened city alley, he actually had a rat run over his foot. Bennett was so upset that he lost bladder control. So this was no ordinary fear.

In a true act of bravery, Bennett disclosed this secret quirk to Mandy. She didn't poke fun at him nor lose her regard for him. Instead, she (as a psychology major, herself) insisted that Bennett seek psychological help for his phobia. To Bennett's great relief, a psychologist was able to help him, and within a brief period of time his lifelong morbid fear was a thing of the past.

Describe your favorite/best:

Food ______

Movie ______

Book ______

Memory ______

Place ______

Vacation ______

Teacher ______

Friend ______

Home ______

Birthday party ______

Dream ______

Describe your happiest moment (do not include times with your partner here) ______

Describe your worst/least favorite:

Food ______

Movie ______

Book ______

Memory ______

Place ______

Vacation ______

Teacher ______

Friend ______

Home ______

Birthday party ______

Nightmare ______

Describe your saddest moment ______

List your major fears. ______

How do you cope with your fears? ______

List your prejudices. (This list can include groups of people, belief systems, activities, etc.)

______

How do you cope with your prejudices? ______________________________

____

Are there any behaviors, idiosyncrasies, or beliefs of others that you find especially obnoxious? Y/N ____ If so, what are they? ______________________________

____

Does your fiancé exhibit any of these? Y/N____ Which ones? ______________________________

____

A Question of Belief: Religion/Ethics/Morality

"All marriages are mixed marriages." — Chantal Saperstein

These are confusing times. On the one hand, there is a steadily rising number of interfaith marriages. At the same time, trends point to people endorsing and adhering more strictly to orthodox observances of various faiths. And while it is certainly possible to have very successful interfaith marriages, for some couples, failing to handle religious differences with mutual respect and sensitivity could mean lots of trouble.

The way you feel about your own faith or religion, if you have one, is important. It can also be very important for people who have chosen not to practice a religion, or to have any religious belief, to have their opinions respected.

Some people regard these matters as paramount in their lives; for others it is less important. But generally speaking, everyone wants to have their feelings and beliefs, whatever they are, respected by others and most especially by the people to whom they are closest.

Religion, especially organized religion, can be all-pervasive in the lives of some individuals. For others it can be incidental, tangential, or important yet perfunctory.

As couples prepare for a life together, religious similarities and differences can be powerful forces that can either bring the couple closer together or can cause problems between them. Whether religion is a strongly held personal belief or merely the practice of a cultural tradition, couples who are planning to marry are advised to discuss their religious beliefs with each other, and where there are differences, find ways to reconcile them.

Beyond religious identification, there are questions of one's own personal ethical beliefs (including the ethics governing interpersonal relationships) and morality (our own internal compasses, which provide us with our own sense of right vs. wrong).

The words "ethics" and "morality" are often used interchangeably. Both describe the implicit rules that guide our interactions with others and our feelings about ourselves as people. Some might argue that without religious underpinnings, there would be no ethics or morality. Others very persuasively argue that nonbelievers/atheists can and do have ethical and moral structures that guide them independent of any belief in a higher power.

It's important to realize that homogeneity does not predict marital bliss and heterogeneity does not dictate failure. Couples who do not share a common set of religious beliefs and practices can, and many do, live together in peaceful harmony. But in such cases it is important that they give some time prior to marriage to exploring what their differences are, discovering any areas of potential conflict, and identifying ways to avoid misunderstandings and difficulties.

Likewise, a couple who has identical religious beliefs when they marry may run into trouble down the line when one partner changes, if the other partner is not flexible enough to absorb the changes and the differences. Finally, even people who share the same basic belief system may think, believe, and behave differently in a variety of specific circumstances. This can cause trouble too, especially if one of you believes that your religion dictates a different kind of response.

Of potentially greater consequence to a couple than religious differences are different opinions concerning ethical standards and moral underpinnings. How you interact with each other, those close to you, and the world at large will reflect your ethics and morals, whether you are a religious person or not.

But remember: a major ingredient and predictor of marital harmony is mutual respect, especially in areas where you disagree.

The following questions are designed to help you examine the details and the depths of your moral, ethical, and religious beliefs. These questions are not just about the person you are but also about the person you aspire to be, and this process is part of a lifelong journey. Sharing your replies with your partner can lead to serious conversations that will help you understand each other in a profoundly important way. It can also influence who your children will become when you, as their parents, provide them with a model for your interactions with each other and with the outside world.

GEORGE AND MARIANNE

For George it wasn't a question of which religion to believe in. He didn't believe in following any religion. Marianne claimed this was not a problem for her. Secretly, she "just knew" that George would come around, once he saw what a source of strength, grounding, and stability religion played in her life. Marianne was virtually certain that he would become inspired, as she had been as a young teen, and that he would come to share her religious beliefs.

George and Marianne dated for several months and eventually declared their mutual love and intention to marry. But as they began to plan their wedding and the matter of choosing an officiant came up, suddenly this long dormant issue was front and center. George was adamant about religion playing no role in their ceremony. Marianne, just as steadfastly, insisted that their nuptials be blessed by God in a way that affirmed her religious beliefs.

Would this standoff have been more easily resolved if they had addressed the issue earlier? Most likely each would have been at least as insistent about their position. But Marianne felt she had time on her side, as well as their love working for her. She was all the more certain that George would eventually change because he did not adhere to some other religion. What she didn't understand was that George's atheism was just as important to him as her religious beliefs were for her. And it was just as likely for him to change his feelings about religion as it was for her to do so. George felt that he had made his feelings clear from the outset of their relationship, and had assumed that Marianne's silence on the subject reflected her tolerance for his lack of belief.

The couple decided that a consultation with an impartial psychologist was a natural next step to preserving their plans for a life together. Despite couples therapy and "good faith" efforts on both their parts the couple decided that they were not ready to proceed with their plans to wed.

Questions About Religion

What religious traditions, if any, were you exposed to as a child? ______________________

____

What is your current religious affiliation? ______________________________________

What are your current religious practices? ______________________________________

____

Do you pray? Y/N ___ If yes, where do you pray? ______________________________

How often do you pray? ____

What religious practices or traditions do you hope to share with your partner in your home?

____

____

What religious practices or traditions do you hope to share with your partner outside the home? ____

____

Unimportant									Very Important
1	2	3	4	5	6	7	8	9	10

Using the scale above, how important to you is it that *your partner* practices or observes your religion

In your home? ______________________ At your place of worship? ____________________

Will this expectation change with the arrival of children? Y/N ___

Please explain ____

Does your partner expect you to practice or observe his or her religion

In your home? ___________________ At his/her place of worship? ____________________

Does this present any problems for you? ____

Do you expect that your partner's expectations will change with the arrival of children?

Y/N ___ Please explain ____

If you have children, do you hope to expose them to certain religious traditions and beliefs?

Y/N ___ If yes, which ones? ____

Which activities/rituals (e.g., baptism, circumcision, first communion, religious school, bar/bat mitzvah, confirmation, observance of religious holidays) do you wish your children to be involved in? ____

____

Questions About Ethics/Morality

On the following scale, how closely do you conform to your own internal standard for ethical and moral behavior?

Weak Conformance — Strong Conformance

1 2 3 4 5 6 7 8 9 10

How important is the gap, if any, between your ideal and your standard? ____________

What are your moral/ethical strengths? ____

____

What are your moral/ethical weaknesses? ____

____

Using the scale above, how well do you believe your partner measures up to *your* standards?

____

What are your partner's moral/ethnical strengths? ____________________________

Where does your partner fall short? ____

How important is this disparity to you? ____

____

How do you hope to reconcile this disparity? ____________________________________

____

When you present yourselves to the outside world as a couple, whose moral/ethical standard do you wish to prevail, and under what circumstances? ____________________________

____

Can you think of an example of when the moral/ethical differences between the two of you were significant, or caused some kind of conflict? Y/N ___ Please explain ________________

____

How was this resolved? ____

____

Can you imagine a future circumstance in which a moral/ethical dilemma might present itself in your life as a couple? ____

____

How do you hope to address this? ____

What are some of the matters about which you have very strong moral/ethical feelings? (Put a check mark next to the ones about which you have strong feelings. Then explain what those feelings are in the space provided.)

___ Abortion ____

___ Birth control ____

___ Capital punishment ____

___ Cheating on taxes ____

___ Cheating (in general) ____

___ Homosexuality ____

___ Illicit drug use ____

___ Lying ____

___ Petty theft ____

___ Sexual infidelity ____

___ Other ____

Secrets

"Secrecy means evasion, and evasion means a problem to the moral mind..." — Gilbert Parker

No, you don't have to, nor is it realistic to reveal everything to your partner. But it's often, though not always, advisable to tell them about most matters of significant importance. (See "Prior Relationships/ Marriages" for more on this)

Revealing our secrets to each other is one way to feel closer. When we share our secrets, we automatically lower the barriers between us and allow the person we are sharing confidences with to be our most special, most intimate "other."

Disclosure of secrets is not guaranteed to be relationship enhancing, but nondisclosure often causes much worse problems than even very difficult disclosures.

If you are unsure about whether or not to reveal one of your secrets to your partner, ask yourself, "Would my partner be damaged by this revelation?" (If so, a good follow-up question is "Will telling my partner about this help her/him? Or will it help me?")

Another thing to consider is whether your partner is likely to learn about your secret from someone else. (If so, it's probably best for him or her to hear about it from you.) Also ask yourself, "Would I want to know this if it were my partner's secret, not mine?"

Then proceed. With caution. With caring. With courage!

CRYSTAL AND JOHNNY

The invitations were sent out, wedding presents were piled up, and the wedding planner was going full tilt. However, Crystal's secret was not out, and it was troubling her. She knew that she should disclose to Johnny that she'd been married, very briefly, fresh out of high school. Granted, this was many years ago, and the time had never seemed right to reveal this unpleasant memory. The longer her story remained untold, the harder it was to disclose it, and the bigger her secret grew in her imagination. Finally Crystal knew no peace. She felt Johnny deserved to hear about this unpleasant chapter in her life. He'd been very open with her and she with him, except for this one thing.

Crystal's parents knew about the deception and had actually encouraged her in the secrecy. They feared it might unnecessarily scare Johnny off. The marriage had ended in an annulment, so in a way it didn't count, was their view. Still, Crystal worried; this didn't exactly seem to her like the best way to start a marriage.

Crystal knew that she couldn't hide behind her fear of exposure, nor could she blame her parents for her lack of candor. While it was very late in the wedding calendar countdown, she finally got the courage to make her disclosure to Johnny. He took in the information slowly and carefully. He asked a number of questions—both about Crystal's first marriage and about her decision to be less than forthcoming with him. He asked for a day to mull things over but returned to her that very evening. He would be fine, he reassured her, "But, please, no more secrets."

I am ashamed of the time I... ___

I am proud of the time I... ___

I regret the time I... ___

Other secrets you choose to keep: ___

___

Is it okay to keep secrets? Y/N ___ If yes, under what circumstances? ___

___

The following questions are about lying:

Is it okay to lie? Y/N ___ If yes, please describe when you think it is okay to lie. ___

___

If yes, what kinds of things is it okay to lie about? ___

If yes, to whom is it okay to lie, and under what circumstances? ___

How would you feel if you found out your partner was lying to you? ___

Is it okay for your partner to lie to anyone? If so, to whom? ___

Is it okay for your partner to lie about anything? If so, about what? ___

The following questions inquire about private communications:

What would you *not want* to be kept private from you by your spouse? ___

___

What would you *want* to be kept private from you by your spouse? ___

___

Are there any things that you would like your partner to share with you but that you will not share with him or her (e.g., details about past relationships, financial history, health history, legal problems)? ___

___

What things is it okay for your partner to choose *not* to share with you but that you *are* willing to share with him or her (e.g., details about past relationships, financial history, health history, legal problems)? ___

___

What rules do you wish to apply for confidences entrusted to you by others? For example, is it okay for you to share these confidences with your partner? Y/N ___ Please explain. ___

___

If confidences are entrusted to your partner by others, would you want your partner to share them with you? Y/N ___ Please explain. ___

___

Would you understand if your partner explained to you that someone had shared something with him or her in confidence and had specifically requested that they ***not*** share it with anyone else? Y/N ___ Please explain. ____

____

The following addresses how the two of you will share confidences entrusted to each other by each other:

Is it okay for *you* to share these with others? Y/N ___ Please explain in what circumstances it would be okay, and with whom: ____

____

Is it okay for *your partner* to share these confidences with anyone else? Y/N ___ Please explain in what circumstances it would be okay, and with whom: ______________________________

____

Sexuality

"If sex is such a natural thing, how come there are so many books on how to do it?" — Bette Midler

"Sex lies at the root of life, and we can never learn to reverence life until we know how to understand sex." — Henry Ellis

For most couples, one of the defining features of their love and commitment to each other is their sexual fidelity.

Sex is loaded with meaning, but it doesn't mean the same thing to everyone.

Sex is a means of communication. Sometimes it goes beyond where words can go; sometimes it is used instead of words to express feelings.

Sex can help couples grow closer, forgive each other for wrongs done, ask for forgiveness, console each other, celebrate good times, find comfort in times of grief.

During sex two individual souls combine their physical and spiritual energies, and their bodies, and act as one. Sex can allow two prickly, hypercritical porcupine-like beings to soften their approach to each other, relax their defenses, and be as one.

Sex can also be the glue that holds a couple together when the gale-force-like winds of the world seem to conspire against them and would otherwise tear them apart. In a world that sometimes makes us feel solitary and embattled, sex can make us feel less alone.

And let's face it. Most of the time, for most people, having sex is fun!

But, for all its wondrous attributes, a good sexual relationship still requires work. A concerted and ongoing effort is required in order for sex between longtime partners not to grow stale. Yes, in the area of sexuality, effort is required to demolish barriers between people rather than build them, to foster understanding versus misunderstanding.

And despite what the poets, romance writers, or lyricists would have you believe, even "good" sex must be tended to—weeded and fertilized like the precious garden it can be. However, unlike a flower garden, where there are certain invariable rules that tend to bring the same results time after time, varying your approach to the care and feeding of your sexual garden can be of essential importance if it is to flourish.

The questions that follow are just the first step in this process. As the years go by, these questions, and others, will need to be revisited, and the answers will likely need to be revised if you wish your sexual garden of pleasure to continue to flower.

RALPH AND DEBBIE

It began innocently enough. Ralph was drawn into an Internet site by a photograph of an incredibly attractive, almost irresistible woman. He then found a link to another site. Soon he was seeing women and men engaged in all kinds of exotic sexual activities.

Some were acts he'd fantasized about, while others were beyond his imagination. Ralph began to feel drawn to this and other porn sites almost each time he logged onto the Internet. It became a habit and began to absorb much of his time. He began to neglect his schoolwork, his time with Debbie, and his sleep. Ralph had a very hard time understanding the genuine, almost palpable pull he felt toward these sites. It was as if he were being sucked into the vortex of this porn addiction. Ralph knew he had a problem but was reluctant to acknowledge it and didn't know what to do about it.

Ralph actually felt some measure of relief when Debbie stumbled upon the porn sites. She had borrowed his computer because her own laptop's hard drive had crashed. Ralph initially was indignant when she asked him about the porn sites. He then became remorseful and asked for her understanding. Debbie, however, didn't understand. She saw his habit as depraved and degrading to women. She wanted Ralph to stop looking at these sites and to surrender his computer passwords to her. She wanted him to allow her full access to his e-mails as well as his search histories. Debbie began to believe that Ralph was not only in the grips of a bad habit (as he put it) but, perhaps, was not a good person. At this point Ralph and Debbie accused each other of bad faith. They sought out a therapist but neither got the concessions from the other that they sought. Both were certain that they were right and the other was wrong, and neither was able to move toward some type of compromise. Their wedding plans were called off.

JUDY AND BUD

Judy and Bud had been sexually intimate for more than a year, yet they still hadn't felt comfortable with the "frequency question," or, as Judy put it, the "frequency problem." Judy consistently felt greater sexual desire than Bud did. Initially Bud ascribed his lack of interest in making love to his stressful job and long hours. Judy's job, however, was also stressful and her hours at work, including her commute, were actually longer than Bud's.

Bud did some soul-searching and realized that he had lost interest in sexual intimacy, in general. The more he thought about it, in fact, the less interested he became. Bud asked Judy to help him with this problem. He said he needed to feel less pressure from Judy; yet, paradoxically, he was also requesting that she act "sexier." He wanted her to dress in a way that was more sexy, to watch erotic movies with him, and to talk about intimate topics. He felt that their home had become antiseptic, and this was a turn-off for him. Judy was relieved to hear these disclosures from Bud. It was a relief to even broach the topic. She tried hard to do as Bud had asked.

Unfortunately, what Bud said he wanted and Judy's sense of the changes he was requesting only intensified the sexual tension and confusion between them. They

> solicited a referral from Judy's gynecologist for a male sex therapist because Bud felt he'd be more comfortable talking about this with a man. The therapy was difficult for a while. But the couple got through it and, at the other end, found increased intimacy and more honesty in their relationship. Bud came to recognize that he had been putting a lot of unnecessary pressure upon himself to perform and that he had been buying into an unreasonable standard that was keeping him from being interested in sex. As he demanded less perfection from himself, he came to be in touch with his own desires. This was extremely helpful in resolving Judy and Bud's "frequency problem." They became a very happy couple.

How frequently do you wish to be sexually intimate with your partner? ____________________

____

How much time you would like to devote to lovemaking (per session and per week)?__________

____

What setting or settings do you prefer for intimate time with your partner? _______________

____

Where and when do you prefer *not* to be intimate (e.g., parents' houses, outdoors, in front of an open window)? ____

____

What would you like to *include* in your lovemaking (e.g., music, erotica or pornography, sex toys, lingerie, massage, special oils, your sexual fantasies, etc.)? ____________________________

____

What would you prefer to *exclude*? (e.g., next-door neighbor, pets, oral sex, anal sex, pornography)? ____

____

Using the scale below how would you describe your libido (sexual drive)? ___

Very Weak									Very Strong
1	2	3	4	5	6	7	8	9	10

What do you wish this level to be? ___

Using the same scale, how would you describe your partner's libido? ___

What would you wish this level to be? ___

Less Than Others									Much More Than Others
1	2	3	4	5	6	7	8	9	10

Using the scale above, how do you believe your libido compares to that of

Other members of your sex ____

Other members of your age group ____

Your friends ____

Your partner ____

Describe your ideal intimate date. ______________________________

____

The following questions ask you to describe your sexual preferences (please be specific):

How, where, and when do you wish to be touched in the course of lovemaking? __________

____

Where do you prefer *not* to be touched? ______________________________

____

How, where, and when do you wish to touch your partner? ______________________________

____

How, where, and when do you wish *not* to touch your partner? ______________________________

____

What sounds do you wish to include in foreplay and lovemaking? ______________________________

____

What sounds do you not like to hear? ______________________________

____

What visual images enhance your lovemaking experience? ______________________________

____

What images detract from your lovemaking experience? ______________________________

When is it appropriate (or exciting) for your partner to remove his/her clothing? __________

____

When is it appropriate for you to remove your clothing? ______________________________

____

Is there any kind of clothing that you would like your partner to wear to enhance lovemaking? ______________________________

____

Is there a type of clothing that you would like to wear to enhance lovemaking? __________

____

Are there any special scents that you particularly like (perfume/cologne/scented lotions, etc.)? ______________________________

Are there any smells that turn you off (incense, body odor, perfume, nail polish, cigarette or cigar smoke, other)? ______________________________

What are your feelings about erotica (and/or pornography) in general? For example if your partner likes to look at, read, or listen to it, does that seem insulting or demeaning to you, as if you're not sufficiently exciting for your partner? Or might it be an enhancement to lovemaking? ________

____

How do you feel about the use of erotica

As part of your lovemaking? ____

Separately, by your partner alone?____

Separately, by yourself alone? ____

What kinds of erotica, if any, would you like to *include* in your lovemaking? ____________

____

What kinds of erotica, if any, would you prefer to *exclude*? ____________________

____

Do you have any sexual thoughts, or do you engage in any sexual behaviors that trouble you? Y/N ___ If "yes," please elaborate____

____

Do you have any sexual thoughts, or do you engage in any sexual behaviors that might trouble your partner ? Y/N ___If yes, please elaborate. ____

____

____

Are there any sexual behaviors of your *partner* that trouble you? Y/N ___ If yes, please elaborate. ____

____

How do you feel about masturbation (self-stimulation) when you are alone? ____________

____

Do you have any reservations about the frequency or method of your masturbation?

Y/N ___ If yes, please elaborate: ____

____

How do you feel about your partner masturbating when he or she is alone? ____________

____

Do you have any reservations about the frequency of your partner's masturbation? Y/N ___ If yes, please explain. ____

How do you feel about stimulating yourself during lovemaking with your partner? __________

____

How do you feel about your partner stimulating him or herself when you are making love?

____

Does your partner have a problem with either of you using self-stimulation during lovemaking? Y/N ___If so, how do you think you could resolve this problem? ______________________________

____

How do you feel about your partner looking at or admiring other members of your sex?

____

How do you feel about your partner's possible attraction to others? ____________________

____

The following questions are about the issue of fidelity:

How would you define "fidelity"? ______________________________

____

How would you define "infidelity"? ______________________________

Unimportant								Very Important	
1	2	3	4	5	6	7	8	9	10

Using the scale above, indicate how important you feel it is for *you* to be faithful to your partner. ____ Please explain. ______________________________

Now indicate how important you feel it is for *your partner* to be faithful to you. ____ Please explain. ______________________________

Do you accept the concept of an "open marriage" (i.e., marriage partners having other sexual liaisons)? Y/N ___ If yes, please explain. ______________________________

____

How would you feel if your partner had an affair? ______________________________

____

Could you forgive your partner if he or she had an affair? Y/N ___ What do you think would be necessary in order for you to resolve your feelings? ______________________________

____

Do you think you would ever have an affair? Y/N ___ If yes, under what circumstances?

____

____

The following questions inquire about manner of dress:

Using the following scale, what is your opinion of your partner's choice of clothing and how he or she wears it? ____

Too Conservative				Just Right					Too Immodest
1	2	3	4	5	6	7	8	9	10

Please explain.____

Using the same scale, how would you describe your own choice of clothing and how you wear it? ______ Please explain. ____

____

The following questions are about public behaviors that might be construed as sexual or erotic:

If you could change your partner's behavior with others, what would you change (e.g., flirtatious behavior)? ____

Is there any way in which you would be willing to alter your own behavior with others in order to make your partner feel more comfortable or happier? ____

____

How do you feel about publicly expressing affection? ____

____

Are there times and places where this is okay? (e.g., at home with family, in public, etc.)

____

Are there times and places where this is *not* okay? ____

Trust and Truthfulness

"The truth is rarely pure and never simple" — Oscar Wilde

Maintaining trust between couples is of paramount importance for marital success. However, in order to maintain trust, we need to be able to rely on our partners for a sense of safety. If there is a breach of trust, particularly if it is major, or there are repeated breaches, it can be devastating to the relationship. Once trust has been broken there is the likelihood that suspicion will enter the relationship, or that the other partner may engage in similar breaches of trust, leading to a rather unpleasant downward spiral.

Conversely, consistency in truthfulness creates a relaxed and secure environment; one that fosters a healthy, happy relationship.

GAIL AND SETH

Gail was certain she wanted children and that Seth would, too. Seth, however, had said, in no uncertain terms, that he did not want children. He explained in joint consultation with his therapist that he already had three children from a prior marriage and that was quite enough for him.

Nonetheless Gail and Seth did marry. And during their first couple of years of marriage, despite Gail's pleas and protests, Seth repeatedly affirmed his previously stated position about not wanting to father any more children. Certain that she was right, and that Seth would change his mind, Gail secretly had her IUD removed, and they conceived a child. Gail gave birth, and Seth did *not* change his mind. He declared that he felt betrayed and left the marriage.

Where and from whom did you learn about trust and truthfulness? ____________________

____

How would you describe the message(s) you received? ____________________

____

Describe a situation where you have broken trust with someone other than your partner.

____

If you could revisit this situation, how would you have behaved differently? ____________________

____

Describe a situation in which you have broken trust with your partner. ____________________

____

If you could revisit this situation, how would you have behaved differently? ____________________

____

Use the following scale to answer the questions that follow.

Not at all important									Highest importance
1	2	3	4	5	6	7	8	9	10

How much value do you place on truthfulness? _______ (A)

How much value do you place on others' truthfulness? _______ (B)

How much value do you place on your fiancé's truthfulness? _____ (C)

How do you wish your fiancé to answer the three questions above using the same scale?

A. ________

B. ________

C. ________

Do you think there are any areas in which complete candor is not called for, or might even be harmful to a relationship? Y/N___ Please explain ____

____

How would you heal from a situation in which your trust in your partner had been broken?

____

____

Work/Career: A Balancing Act

"I think work is the world's greatest fun" — Thomas Edison

Freud described life's major tasks as "to love and to work."

For some people work is merely a means to an end; that is, the purpose of work is to be able to generate sufficient income to sustain oneself and his or her dependents.

For others, it is an important way of defining oneself. It's "who I am"—a policeman, a fire chief, a chef, a teacher, an artist, a doctor, a lawyer, a stay-at-home mom (or dad).

How you and your partner feel about the importance of work in your lives can be crucial in establishing a balanced life and maintaining a healthy relationship.

Depending on the kind of work we do, work can provide an opportunity for being creative, generous, outgoing, and people-focused, or introspective and private. Work provides a space in our lives that can be inspiring or depleting.

While to some degree all of us define ourselves through our work, for the sake of ourselves and those we love we should not allow our work to *totally* define us or to distort the balance in the rest of our lives.

Assigning work its appropriate place in our lives is an ongoing challenge. If left unmonitored, career goals and the demands of work may well take over the lives of less vigilant couples. Working toward a common financial goal, the allure of professional recognition, the pressure of pursuing promotions, etc., can erode a couple's resolve to maintain a healthy work/life/family balance.

But a full and rewarding life consists of work *plus* many other deserving activities and pursuits. If we fail to keep work in its proper place, we can unwittingly neglect the things we value most: our marriages, our children, our extended family, our health, our communities.

A major consideration for most couples is the allocation of time and effort devoted to work versus home life. There will be times when work will present demands that are beyond our control (think of an accountant in early April or a farmer protecting crops from a sudden, early frost). However, the concessions we make that create the "little murders" of a relationship are usually more predictable and recurring. Planning ahead about how to handle these crises will be useful for any couple, and having had hypothetical discussions beforehand will be helpful when actual situations arise.

Does our work make us feel bigger or smaller, generous or selfish, outwardly focused or self-focused? Do we want to be expansive and exploratory, or do we want to withdraw and avoid risk? How does the nature of our work bring out the best in us and help us to minimize our less admirable traits and characteristics? These are all questions to think about when making career choices, but they also have an important place in looking ahead to how the work of two individuals will make life easier or more difficult for a couple.

HAROLD AND CARMEN

The quintessential question for dual-income, newly marrieds can often boil down to questions of whose job is more important, and what is "fair." Harold and Carmen actually did have this discussion before they married. And they had it again and again. The problem was, the discussions didn't seem to be resolving anything, and the questions they were discussing were by nature very difficult to resolve. What constitutes the basis for fairness? What makes one job more important than another? Is it about higher income? Whose turn is it to make the sacrifice? Whose job is more promising in terms of career goals? The number of variables to consider seemed infinite to Harold and Carmen, and they weren't even married yet; so far, it was an exercise in hypotheticals.

For example, Harold wanted to know how Carmen would feel if he were promoted in his government contracting job but was also transferred to a too-far-to-commute-to city. In answer, Carmen recounted her pet peeve from childhood. Her mom would always stay home for Carmen and her siblings when they were ill and too young or sick to stay home alone. Why, she would ask herself, was it never her dad? She wondered if Harold would be willing to apply a different standard for their future children.

Both Carmen and Harold felt stymied by their discussions. They were caught up in the emotions of what they imagined army generals experienced when engaged in war games exercises.

What Carmen and Harold were missing, their minister told them, was the opportunity to make use of these hypothetical, but certainly not implausible, dilemmas. The minister wanted to convey the notion of the marriage being a place for generosity and self-sacrifice, which he saw as an essential link in the marital bond. The hypothetical problems they were posing to each other, and a host of others to come would provide the couple with the chance to demonstrate their love and commitment to their union. The hypothetical dilemmas, when they actually arose, could afford them a chance to give to each other.

Both Harold and Carmen warmed to this principle, and their subsequent discussions ignited what felt like a burning desire to give, not reflexively, but thoughtfully. They were introduced to the notion of "what would be best for *us,* not me" as a guiding principle. They took this principle to heart and went on to form a mutually fulfilling marriage.

Using the scale below how committed are you to your career?

Not Very Committed — Very Committed

1 2 3 4 5 6 7 8 9 10

Do you think your career aspirations will negatively impact other aspects of your life? Y/N ___ Which aspects? ______________________________

If so, how do you feel about that? ____

____

Do you expect to (check all that apply.)

Work after you are married ____

Work part-time ____

Work full-time ____

Stay home with the kids: Permanently _____ Temporarily _____ Part-time _____ Full-time _____

Do you expect your partner to

Work after you are married ____

Work part-time ____

Work full-time ____

Stay home with the kids: Permanently _____ Temporarily _____ Part-time _____ Full-time _____

Please indicate the priority, in numerical order, in which you *currently place* each of the following (1 = highest):

____ Work

____ Play

____ Marriage/romantic relationship

____ Social relationships

____ Family

____ Community service

____ Fitness

____ Other _______________

Which of these numbers would you be willing to change? And under what conditions do you think a change in your priorities would be called for? ______________________________

Now return to the list and describe how you would *like to* live your life, possibly reordering your priorities.

____ Work

____ Play

____ Marriage/romantic relationship

____ Social relationships

____ Family

____ Community service

____ Fitness

____ Other _______________

Returning to the list, next describe how you wish *your fiancé* would choose to order his/her priorities.

____ Work

____ Play

____ Marriage/romantic relationship

____ Social relationships

____ Family

____ Community service

____ Fitness

____ Other_________

What if your lists differ? (They probably will!) How do you think you can resolve these differences if they begin to intrude upon your happiness/contentment? ________________________________

____

Respond to the following dilemma: Presuming that both of you are working outside the home, who should stay home when the children are ill, or have a snow day, or a day off from school? _______

____

____

Other Relationships (It's Not Just the Two of You!)

"You don't choose your family. They are God's gift to you, as you are to them." — Desmond Tutu

Now is the time to examine family relationships and what they mean to you, for better or worse, and to share some of those feelings and experiences with your partner.

Most everyone has at least one "crazy uncle," a relative who is the subject of much mirth, cringing, or eye-rolling, sometimes viewed fondly by the family, sometimes not so fondly.

There are also people in our lives that are anything but an embarrassment. They have been instrumental in forming our most fundamental characteristics and values. They have contributed greatly to making us who we are and what we stand for. Introducing these special people to your partner and explaining how and why they are important to you can be essential to your partner coming to understand the real "you," the person he or she will be marrying.

After all, eventually your partner will probably be meeting all of them. Isn't it best for him or her to be prepared?

GERALDINE AND TOMMY

Geraldine did not have any felons, underworld figures, or celebrities as direct relations. She did, however, have an unusual family structure. She had what she considered two families: she was adopted and had two older brothers, the biological offspring of her two adoptive parents. In her adoptive family she also had an uncle and aunt on her father's side, two uncles and an aunt on her mother's, and within her generation she had eight first cousins.

When she was six, her parents told her that she was adopted. Geraldine felt fine with this. She had a friend who was also adopted, so it didn't seem weird. However, at age eleven, she was informed that her biological parents, who were not married when she was born, had subsequently married. When she was sixteen, they contacted her adoptive parents and asked them to meet with Geraldine. This was a lot for a sixteen-year-old to handle, but she ventured forth and got to know her two biological parents and two younger sisters, ages four and two.

This was going to be a lot to explain to her fiancé, Tommy, who had the most traditional of family structures. Geraldine was not at all ashamed of her background; she thought it made her "interesting." However, she knew that Tommy's family might not be quite so accepting of the situation. She did the best she could to explain how she felt about *all* of her family, and Tommy did his best to respect all of these relationships.

Parents

"Parents are the last people on earth who ought to have children." — Samuel Butler

Let's face it, we'd be nowhere without them. And yet...

For some families, disruption caused by divorce, estrangement, illness, or, even death has had a profound and negative effect on family dynamics. For others, it's relatively smooth sailing.

But many people, even people who have essentially positive relationships with their parents, have had a less-than-perfect history or less-than-happy relationships with their parents at some points in the past.

Whatever our own personal family history, each of us has had a unique experience, and to be well understood by your fiancé, some appreciation of the history and character of your current relationship with your family is in order. This history is the background onto which the tapestry of your life is woven.

Questions About Parents

Describe your parents' personalities.

Mother ____

Father ____

Describe your relationship with your parents.

Mother

Past ____

Present ____

Father

Past ____

Present ____

How frequently do you have contact with your parents?

Telephone calls ____________

Visits ____________

E-mails/text messages ____________

Other ____________

Do you wish to maintain the same amount of time and communication with your parents after you are married? Y/N ___ Please explain. ____________________________

Do you have any concerns about this, or do you think your partner will? Y/N ___ Please explain.

____

Describe the relationship you want your partner to have with your parents. ____________

____

What frequency of contact with your family do you expect your partner to find comfortable?

Telephone calls ____________________

Visits ____________________

E-mails/text messages ____________________

Other ____________________

How much time does your partner spend with his or her parents? ____________________

Are you comfortable with this amount of time? Y/N ___ If no, do you think it should be more, or less? ____________________

Questions About Stepparents

"The fear of every stepparent is that they really ***are*** *a monster." — Yvonne Roberts*

Describe who your stepparents are by name, as well as to whom they are (or were) married.

____

Describe their personalities. ____________________

____

Describe your relationship with your stepparent(s) past and present. ____________________

____

Describe the kind of relationship you wish to have with your stepparents in the future.

____

How often do you have contact with your stepparents?

Visits ____________________

Telephone calls ____________________

E-mails/text messages ____________________

Other ____________________

Questions About Grandparents

"Perfect love sometimes does not come until the first grandchild." — Welsh Proverb

"The idea that no one is perfect is a view most commonly held by people with no grandchildren." — Doug Larson

Describe your grandparents by name and by their relationship to your parents (e.g., Mom's mom, Dad's dad, etc.). ____________________

____

____

Describe their personalities. ____

____

Describe your relationship with your grandparents, past and present. ______________

____

____

How often do you have contact with your grandparents?

Visits ____________________

Telephone calls ________________

E-mails/text messages _________________

Other ____________________

Describe the kind of relationship you wish to have with your grandparents in the future.

____

____

Questions About Your Future In-laws

"Behind every successful man stands a surprised mother-in-law." — Voltaire

How frequently do you wish to have contact with your future in-laws?

Telephone calls ____________________

Visits ____________________

E-mails/text messages ____________________

Other ____________________

Describe the kind of relationship you wish to have with them in the future. ______________

____

Questions About Aging Parents

"A test of a people is how it behaves toward the old...the affection and care for the old, the incurable, the helpless, are the true gold mines of a culture." — Abraham J. Heschel

What are your expectations/fears regarding the care of your aging parents (or parent substitutes), as they grow older? (e.g., Do you think they should move closer to you, or that you should move closer to them? Have you ever thought that one day they might move into your place, or next door? Will they need financial support?) ____

____

____

Have you and your partner talked about these matters? Y/N ___ Do you agree about how these kinds of matters should be handled? Y/N ___ Please explain. ______________________________

____

Children (From Previous Marriages or Prior Relationships)

Questions About Your Children from Prior Relationships

Name	Age	Gender
____________________	______	_____
____________________	______	_____
____________________	______	_____

How do you want your fiancé to relate to your children from a prior relationship? ____________

____

How do you wish your partner to speak with you about, and share information about, your children (for example, observations about their development, study habits, ethical standards, disciplining, any secrets entrusted to them)? ____

____

____

Please describe your children's other parent's personality. ______________________________

____

____

Please describe that parent's current involvement with your children and how, if at all, you would wish to alter it. ____

____

Please describe how you would like your new partner's relationship with your children's other parent to be.

___ polite ___ warm/friendly ___ distant ___ no opinion ___ no relationship

___ other _____________

Questions About Your Partner's Children from a Prior Relationship

"Two myths must be shattered: that of the evil stepparent…and the myth of instant love, which places unrealistic demands on all members of the blended family." — Claire Berman

How do you hope to relate to your future spouse's children from a prior relationship?

____

How do you wish to communicate and share information with your partner about his/her children? ____

How do you hope to relate to the other parent of your future spouse's children? ____________

____

Describe what you know of their other parent's personality. ________________________________

____

Please describe what you know of their other parent's involvement with the children. __________

____

____

How, if at all, would you wish to alter that parent's relationship with the children (i.e., increased or decreased time, disciplining)? ____

____

Siblings, Other Extended Family Members (And Those You Consider "Like Family")

"Our brothers and sisters are there with us from the dawn of our personal stories to the inevitable dusk."
— Susan Scarf Merrell

You may be an only child and your parents may also have been only children, but chances are there are still people in your life, people who feel like family, who could fall into this general category. Let's call them relatives for the sake of this discussion.

So, even if you are an only child of only children, don't skip this section!

List and describe any other family members, describing how close you are to them or were in the past. Add a few descriptive words about their personalities (use extra pages if necessary).

____

____

____

What kind of relationships have you *had* with the primary members of your family in the past? (e.g., close, distant, friendly, antagonistic, uneven?) ______________________________

____

____

____

If your past family history is significantly different from the present, how does this affect your present relationships? What has changed? ______________________________

____

____

What kind of relationships do you wish to have with the members of your immediate family in the future? ______________________________

____

____

How would you like your partner to relate to these family members? Be as specific as possible. ______________________________

____

Add anything else you feel is important to convey to your partner about your family, religious, cultural, or ethnic group that you think will help him/her understand you better.

____

____

What do you wish to ask your partner about his/her family, religious, or ethnic group that might help you understand him/her better? ______________________________

____

Prior Relationships/Marriages

"A wife lasts only for the length of the marriage, but an ex-wife is there for the rest of your life." — Jim Samuels

Many men and women, before they become engaged, have been previously involved in romantic relationships, ranging anywhere from casual to intense, with someone else. These prior relationships may or may not have included some level of sexual involvement.

The absence or presence of a history of previous romance does not necessarily predict the success or failure of any subsequent relationship. But this history can sometimes be the source of curiosity, discomfort, or even jealousy for you or your partner.

Memories and continuing reminders of past romantic and/or sexual relationships can be painful, inspirational, neutral, toxic, or none of the above.

Dealing with these histories can be done collaboratively as you establish your own rules and preferences for the amount and nature of disclosure in this area. It is also, to a great degree, a private matter, and yours to decide. *You* should be allowed to be the one to choose what you think is appropriate and inappropriate to share with your partner. But you will also want to consider the ramifications of what you choose *not* to disclose.

Some of the questions to consider might be: Would this knowledge, once disclosed, be helpful or harmful to us as a couple? Might it make my partner feel less attractive/ jealous/ uncomfortable around the other person (if he/she is still in your life)? Might my partner find out about this matter from someone else? If so, would it be best for me to disclose something about the past relationship to my partner, rather than to have it disclosed by someone else?

JOY AND CAREY (AND DONALD)

One day Donald called Joy from out of the blue. They had been in a very serious relationship during their junior year abroad in Dublin. They had felt something very special, both a deep friendship and a strong physical attraction. This experience had inspired Joy to set the bar far higher for any future relationship than she had in the past. But after their year abroad, they came to realize that their relationship couldn't survive the strain of a bicoastal romance—he in Seattle, she in Richmond. Their relationship ended, yet the positive memories lingered. So it was quite exhilarating for Joy to hear from Donald when he called.

However, Joy was now engaged to Carey. And as much as she wanted to see Donald, she was conflicted. From past experience, she knew that Carey was not fond of meeting or even hearing about her past boyfriends. While they hadn't explicitly agreed to it, neither Joy nor Carey had continued contact with their "ex's" once they'd moved in together.

> Joy didn't wish to hurt either Carey or Donald. She didn't want to rebuff Donald's request that they meet for old times' sake. He'd be in town just briefly and, he explained, he too was in a committed relationship. On the other hand, Joy didn't want to appear to betray Carey by seeing Donald without his knowledge.
>
> So Joy told Carey about Donald's visit, and his request to see her. Carey admitted that his uneasiness was irrational, but asked Joy to respect their understanding anyway. She agreed to comply for Carey's sake, and for the sake of the relationship. After all, she decided, she would want Carey to do the same for her, even if he disagreed with her. She decided that sometimes devotion trumps reasonableness.

What would you like to know about your fiancé's prior relationships/marriage(s)? ____________

____

What would you prefer *not* to know about your fiancé's prior relationships/marriage(s)?

____

____

What would you like to tell your fiancé about your prior romantic relationships/ marriage(s)?

____

____

What would you prefer *not* to divulge about your prior romantic relationships/ marriage(s)?

____

If you fear that this information could be disclosed to your partner by someone else, how would you wish this matter to be addressed, and when? ______________________________

____

____

Do you wish your spouse to cut off or limit contact with prior romantic partners, if possible?
Y/N ___ Please explain. ______________________________
Should this same rule apply to you? Y/N ___ Please explain ______________________________

____

If prior romantic partners are part of your current or potential social circle:

How do you wish to relate to your mate's prior romantic partners? ____________________

____

How do you wish your mate to relate to your prior romantic partners? ________________

____

Assuming that one of the above becomes problematic along the way, how would you wish for you and your mate to deal with any jealousy or other problems that occur? ____________________

____

Friends and Community

No man is an island.... —John Donne

This is true of couples as well. Unless they occupy a deserted island, it is rare that a couple can cut themselves off from the broader community, nor would most couples want to. Humans are social beings: our work, play, worship, and education all tend to bring us together with those who share our interests, goals, and pastimes.

Social interactions can be life-and marriage-enhancing, or they can pose problems for couples. Again, there is no one right way to be. Some couples are happy to have a very limited social life; others thrive on social interaction; in still other couples, the two partners have very different social needs and are happy to let each other interact socially, each to the degree that is comfortable for them.

It is not being identical in this regard that is important, but understanding the nature of each of your needs and desires for social interaction, and being able to respect and support each other in your choices. (Usually trouble comes not from being different from each other, but from having one's expectations disappointed.) If your partner is more or less antisocial now, preferring to avoid parties and other social gatherings, you should not expect that being married will change that. Likewise, if you prefer quiet evenings at home, but your partner loves to party, that is probably not going to change with marriage either; at least these assumptions should not be made.

Some areas that tend to cause concern and/or problems for couples include: How much time should we share with others (and whom do we want to spend our time with)? How much emotional energy will it take? How much income will be spent on various social activities or giving to various organizations? What is the proper balance between couple time vs. individual time spent with others? How involved do you want to be in decisions made about your partner spending time with friends of the opposite sex*? How will you deal with any concerns that arise about this kind of activity?

GRETA AND SAM

Greta and Sam both felt very comfortable with Greta's friends. They had actually met each other through an introduction by Greta's officemate. But Sam's friends were a different story. Greta had never liked them, and they never seemed very welcoming to her (despite the fact that she and Sam had been dating for over a year and had been engaged for three months). Sam's friends, even by Sam's own account, didn't seem to like Greta or approve of them as a couple.

Some of this discord could be explained by the simple fact that most of Greta's friends were either married or seriously dating a special someone. In contrast, Sam's friends were all single. None were dating seriously or seemed to show much interest in being in a serious relationship. Sam's "peeling off from the squadron" (as his friend Mike put it) was interpreted as a defection of sorts, an act of disloyalty. Therefore Greta's presence in their activities wasn't welcome. As difficult as this was for Sam, who valued his old friendships, it was even more of a problem for Greta. She worried that Sam's friends might be a "fifth column," trying to sabotage them as a couple going forward. However, she was not proud of her fears and was reluctant to share them with Sam. She saw herself as insecure and thought that perhaps she was imagining the slights. Sam was similarly a bit embarrassed by his friends' behavior and was reluctant to speak of it to them and to Greta.

Fortunately for the couple, Greta had one of her famous but infrequent "meltdowns." Tearfully, she disclosed her worst imaginings to Sam. Sam was relieved to know how she felt and it helped him to better understand her behavior around his friends. He was quick to reassure her that she was not just imagining things. Subsequently, talking to his dad, Sam learned that this was not such an unusual phenomenon in the natural life of friendships, and that this kind of thing often happens, especially when one member of a group does something ahead of the rest. Sam was reassured to know that while there might be some attrition in his friendships, these friends might become close again once they too found themselves becoming attached to someone special. Clearing the air helped both Greta and Sam feel much better.

Questions About Friends

What level of involvement do you wish to have or maintain with *your* friends after you are married?

Separately ______________________________

As a couple ______________________________

How do you feel about your *partner's* friends?

___ I like them all ___ I like some of them, but not others ___ I am mostly indifferent to them

___ I mostly disapprove of them

Please elaborate, especially if you disapprove of your partner's friends: ______________________________

____

Using the following scale:

Minor level of involvement									Very involved
1	2	3	4	5	6	7	8	9	10

What level of involvement do you find comfortable for your partner to have with his or her friends?

Separate from you ____

Together with you _____

What rules or preferences do you wish to apply to your partner's friendships with members of the opposite* sex?

Regarding time alone with members of the opposite sex (without you there): ____________

____

Regarding time with them, with you present: ____________________

____

How do you feel about your partner going for a boys'/girls'* night out? ____________

____

____

How do you feel about a boys'/girls'* weekend away? ____________________

____

What limits would you wish to apply to the above as to:

Frequency ____________________________________

Duration ____________________________________

Activities ____________________________________

What limits are reasonable to be placed on *you* concerning which friends you see and how often you see them and what you do with them? ____________________

____

Questions About Community Activities

What community activities and/or charitable work are you involved in currently? ____________

____

Do you wish to continue this work or these activities after you are married? Y/N ____

If yes, would you like (or expect) your partner to also become involved in this activity?

Y/N ____ In what way?____________________________

What community activities and/or charitable work is your partner involved in currently?

____

Do you wish for your partner to continue this work or these activities after you are married?

Y/N ____

If yes, would your partner like (or expect) you to also become involved in this activity?

____

Pets

"In order to keep a true perspective of one's importance, everyone should have a dog that will worship him and a cat that will ignore him." — Dereke Bruce

For some people, pets are truly their best friends, like a member of the family. To these people, it seems obvious that pets are worthy of abundant love and extensive investment of time and money.

For others, pets are not highly valued. They can even be seen as annoyances and can become objects of resentment, especially if the pet is seen as a rival for the affection and attention of one's partner. In other cases, the partner may have an allergy or other medical condition that can make living with pets ill advised.

Just as one must be scrupulous in not criticizing or disciplining stepchildren, the same rule applies to your fiancé's pet. This may come as a surprise to some people: beware! Punishing your partner's pets, making disparaging remarks about them, etc., can cause big trouble. On the other hand, your compliments, love, and affection will in most cases be very welcome.

Please note: The analogy between stepchildren and pets is a deliberate one! Pets often serve as a substitute for children for empty-nesters, the childless, or eager parents-to-be.

EILEEN AND ROBINSON

Sylvester, the cat, had been Eileen's companion and confidante ever since junior high school. He was given to her shortly after the divorce of her parents at the same time she went off to live with her mom and her mom's boyfriend in a new city. Her new home was not at all close to where she and her mother and father had lived. Eileen adored her cat, and others often remarked at how much more "doglike" Sylvester was in his sociability and remarkable friendliness.

Robinson was not pet-unfriendly, and he truly took a liking to Sylvester. But as Eileen and Robinson grew together as a couple, Sylvester's disposition seemed to have changed. He snapped at and scratched Robinson on several occasions. It seemed to Robinson that Sylvester was jealous of their relationship. Sadly Sylvester seemed to begin suffering just as Eileen was celebrating her betrothal to Robinson. He was less energetic and seemed to withdraw. The couple was encouraged to see a pet psychologist, who endorsed the diagnosis of jealousy. Several interventions were tried, as was another psychologist. Ultimately, in the context of a consultation with a pastoral counselor, Eileen began the process of finding a new family for Sylvester, since neither Sylvester nor the couple seemed to be thriving in Eileen's new situation. Robinson was counseled to be very respectful and patient during this process. Though it was extremely painful for her emotionally, Eileen recognized that her new life with Robinson was best begun without her beloved pet.

Do you own a pet? Y/N ___ If yes, please describe ______________________________

Do you wish to have a pet when you are married? Y/N ___

If yes, what type? ______________________________

How would you feel about a difference in preference between you and your fiancé? That is, how flexible will you be if your fiancé is strongly opposed to your choice of pet or to *not* having a pet? ______________________________

____

Do you have pet allergies? Y/N ___ Please specify ______________________________

How do you feel about a pet sharing your bed or your food, being kissed by your partner, or kissing you? ______________________________

____

Do you have any fears about pets or aversions to any kind of pet? Y/N ___

If yes, please specify. ______________________________

Using the following scale please answer the following questions about prospective or current pet ownership in your life together.

Unimportant									Very Important
1	2	3	4	5	6	7	8	9	10

If you have a pet, how important is it to you that:

Your partner shares your affection for your pet? _____

Your partner be "approved of" by your pet? _____

If there were a "bad match" between your partner and your pet, what might you do, or be willing to do, to remedy this situation? ______________________________

What will you do if your pet and your partner truly cannot tolerate each other? ______________

____

Special Occasions

Birthdays

"My birthday!—what a different sound
That word had in my youthful ears;
And how each time the day comes round,
Less and less white its mark appears."— Thomas Moore

Why are birthdays so important?

Well, they are and they aren't. Or, they are for some people, and they aren't for others. Then again, some watershed birthdays are very important for some people, and other birthdays, not so much.

For many people, birthdays take on an enormous amount of symbolic importance, especially during our younger years. Birthdays are an opportunity to feel special because, unlike other holidays, they're ours alone.

Birthdays are a time to receive presents from friends and family, perhaps to have a small ceremony (a cake, candles, etc.). In other families, certain milestone birthdays are the occasion for much larger celebrations (quinceanera, bar or bat mitzvahs, sweet sixteen, or coming-of-legal-age). Then, after the age of 21, the excitement tends to die down except for all but those milestone birthdays marked by the decades.

Some people despise all the "hoopla" and prefer to mark their special day quietly, if at all. Their needs and desires should be respected as well.

Most of us have a natural desire to continue celebrating birthdays more or less in the way we have been accustomed to doing, especially if our memories are pleasant ones. Then again, some of us may want to make more of the event than we ever have in the past, especially if we felt deprived as children.

Unfortunately, birthday traditions and personal preferences are not automatically shared by everyone and cannot be guessed. We have to clearly convey our wishes about birthday celebrations to our partners. Otherwise, despite our best intentions these special days can end up in disappointment, hurt feelings, or misunderstandings, rather than celebration and joy.

PAULA AND JEROME

Paula had very set ideas about her birthday. As she was growing up, it had never occurred to her that her preferences were at all unusual. She simply expected to be treated as "special" on this day. "Special" for her meant gifts, a cake, and acknowledgment that this was her day. She didn't expect to be treated as royalty, only as "special."

Jerome came from a large family. Birthdays were not all that special for anyone in his family. He never had a party thrown for him and he had never had a birthday cake. (His mom was definitely not the cake-baking type.) Since he had grown up quite poor, the gifts given were thoughtful but very inexpensive.

This difference in histories between Paula and Jerome made for a clash of expectations, hurt feelings, and bewilderment. Their minister caught a glimpse of this during a marital preparation class. Paula admitted she was a bit hurt that Jerome hadn't made more of a fuss over her birthday earlier in the week. This chance remark provided an opportunity for the couple and the minister to address their different personal histories and expectations. Neither Paula nor Jerome were allowed to either gain the high ground or to beg forgiveness. Instead, the minister seized this moment as an opportunity to talk about the power of expectations (both voiced and silent) as well as how differing familial cultures impact a marriage. The minister pointed out that Paula's hurt feelings could be used as an opportunity for the couple to begin to establish their own new traditions.

Questions About Your Birthday

Using the scale below:

Unimportant									Important
1	2	3	4	5	6	7	8	9	10

How important are birthdays to you? ____

How do you wish to celebrate your next birthday? ________________________________

Whom will you be inviting to your next birthday celebration? ________________________

____

Whom would you *not* want to invite? ______________________________________

____

Where would you like to celebrate your next birthday? ____________________________

How important is it to you to be the focus of the celebration? ______________________

What would you like the level of expense of the celebration to be? ___________________

Describe your favorite birthday memories: ___________________________________

____

Which elements of past birthday celebrations would you like to retain? Which things would you like to change? ____________________

How do you wish to observe your special day beyond having a party? (e.g., day off from work, taking a trip, other thoughts) ____________________

____

Do you like surprise gifts? Y/N ___ Please explain ____________________

What kinds of gifts do you prefer? (practical? frivolous? lavish?) Please explain ____________________

____

To avoid disappointment in the gift(s) you receive, how do you intend to communicate your preferences to your partner? ____________________

____

How much money do you think you and your spouse should spend on gifts for each other?

____

Is there a particular gift you have in mind for your next birthday Y/N? ___ If yes, what?

____

Questions About Your Partner's Birthday

How do you wish to celebrate your partner's next birthday? ____________________

____

Where would you like to celebrate it? ____________________

What do you think your partner would like to do for his or her birthday? ____________________

____

How similar is this to your wishes? ____________________

Does your partner like surprise gifts, parties? Y/N ____ Please explain ____________________

____

How do you decide on a suitable gift for someone?

___ Asking questions of the recipient

___ Asking questions of the recipient's friends or family

___ Intuition

___ Other ____________________

What kind of a gift do you wish to give to your fiancé? (practical? frivolous? lavish?)
Please explain ____________________

Anniversaries

"An anniversary is a time to celebrate the joys of today, the memories of yesterday, and the hopes of tomorrow." — Author unknown

Remembering and recognizing important milestones in a relationship can be very important to a couple. Which anniversaries to commemorate can vary and evolve as you two move on through your years together. Hopefully, over time your individual preferences will meld into mutual preferences.

BETH AND FREDDIE

The stereotype of the guy* forgetting a special date (usually a couple's wedding anniversary) and being in the proverbial doghouse didn't fit Beth and Freddie. First of all, they weren't even married yet. Secondly, they were both women. However, anniversaries were a problem for them anyway...and already. Freddie wanted Beth to make the day they had declared their love for each other to be a celebration. She wanted to dress up, go out, exchange gifts, and make a big deal over each other and about their special bond.

But Beth wasn't that kind of person. She tended toward the understated. She thought that these kinds of celebrations, in general, were not genuine and that hers and Freddie's mutual love should be celebrated every day. It's not that Beth hadn't seen her parents celebrate their wedding anniversary; she just didn't share their temperament.

As the couple discussed this matter, Beth acknowledged that she had seen her parents' celebratory mood as forced and phony. (Her parents did not have a very happy marriage.) It came as an "ah-ha" moment to Beth that her reluctance to be so enthralled with an anniversary celebration was because she had seen her parents' modeling in this regard as fraudulent. Beth and Freddie were working on building the ability to talk things out and trying to understand each other's points of view without the need for one person to be right and the other to be wrong. Freddie tried to temper her expectations of Beth, and Beth began to modestly celebrate the special occasions that were so important to Freddie. They "met in the middle," and in so doing, both felt happier.

Which anniversaries do you want to celebrate?

____ Wedding date

____ Proposal date

____ First date

____ Other (e.g., date when you first met, when you first knew you were in love, etc.)

____

How do you wish to celebrate your special day? ________________________________

____

How do you think your spouse will wish these days to be celebrated? ________________________

____

How do/did your parents or other significant role models celebrate their anniversaries?

____

Would you like to celebrate your anniversary as they did? Y/N ___ Please explain. _____________

____

Holidays

"Holidays in general breed unrealistic expectations. The minute you start wondering, 'Is it going to be wonderful enough?' it never will be." — Pepper Schwartz

You have no idea how problematic holidays can be!

Or maybe you do. Unfortunately, for many people some of those days that are supposed to be exceptionally joyous can be fraught with difficulties and can even become emotional minefields.

Who would think that even Thanksgiving—such a simple, noncommercial, all-inclusive, sweet holiday—would be a time for hurt feelings, disappointments, resentments, feelings of isolation, exclusion, and even despair?

Well, take it from a seasoned psychologist, unfortunately this is true for many, many, people.

Couples are likely to have a lot of work ahead of them as they go about blending, sharing, recasting, and forming their own holiday traditions. This can be hard to do, especially when one or the other partner believes their way is best or that they have a special entitlement for doing it their way.

Religious holidays present the potential for especially challenging holiday clashes. (After all, the original meaning of the word "holiday" comes from "*holy* day.")

Around holidays, the two of you will be impressed by the differences in your religious beliefs and traditions. Even if you share the same faith. personal and family traditions can present difficulties if one or both partners are strongly, even stubbornly, committed to adhering to doing things the way they were done in their families of origin. When are the Christmas presents opened? (On Christmas Eve or Christmas morning?) What kind of seder will be celebrated? (And how rigidly will the rules concerning the preparation of Passover be followed in your home?) Should children be taught to believe in Santa Claus and the Easter Bunny? etc., etc., etc. And it can be much more difficult for couples who do *not* share the same religious identification,

Don't be put off by the differences between you and your partner. And don't be too surprised, or frightened, if your own or your partner's beliefs as to how things must be observed seem occasionally irrational. Holidays bring out the irrational in many of us!

It is natural to have strong feelings about these things. The purpose of talking them over now is so that you can discover the areas of potential conflict, and work on potential solutions well in advance.

Through the years, through trial and error, and within a context of mutual love and respect, your differences can be worked out. Recognizing that no answer to differences between you is necessarily "right" or "best" is an excellent starting point, once these differences, no matter how subtle, are revealed. Who knows? You two might come to establish your own traditions as an expression of your unique efforts to join together and celebrate your union. Stranger things have happened!

DONNY AND ANDY

Donny and Andy were at odds over which family they'd visit for Christmas dinner. Both were brought up in households where early afternoon on Christmas Day was the main attraction, and neither wished to compromise. In addition, each felt family pressure to be there to give a sense of familial unity. Whether it would have been any different were they from large families, they had no idea. However both being only children, the burden seemed even greater to abide by their parents' wishes.

The laws of physics wouldn't allow this couple to be in two different places at the same time. Also, neither wished to be separated, i.e., to go to their separate family celebrations without the other. Both cherished this time of year, saw this holiday as special, and wanted to be together. Also, it was difficult enough being a gay couple; they didn't want to imply that they were less solidly committed than any other engaged couple, either to themselves or to the rest of the world.

A close friend suggested that they include their respective families in helping them solve their dilemma. Andy's family seemed very entrenched: they cited church service schedules and long-standing commitments to attend neighborhood friends' traditional open houses as reasons for being unable to help the couple. Happily, Donny's family was quite sympathetic and offered to move their celebration to Christmas Eve. Donny's folks were able to come up with several advantages to the new arrangement and even spoke of preferring it.

Including others in problem solving can often have surprisingly positive outcomes. Even if the solution isn't readily apparent, this strategy can help convey a couple's concern for the feelings of others and raise awareness in the extended family of the negative impact of placing pressure on couples. This is yet another example of how a couple can engage in the process of creating a model of " we" (versus "me") to their respective families and communities. This can be especially important for nontraditional couples (i.e. gay couples, or those who are ethnically, racially and/or religiously diverse).

Questions About Religious Holidays

Which religious holidays do you celebrate? Please list them in order of their importance to you, with 1 as most important..

Rank	Holiday
______	________________________________
______	________________________________
______	________________________________
______	________________________________
______	________________________________
______	________________________________

Now describe your childhood traditions for each of the holidays you listed. ____________________

____

How do you wish to preserve your childhood or family traditions in your new married life?

If the two of you have conflicts about which holidays to celebrate or how to celebrate them, how do you suggest resolution/reconciliation (e.g., alternating years, spending the holidays apart, celebrating both religious traditions)?

When there are absolute and mutually exclusive conflicts over how to observe religious holidays (e.g., gifts distributed Christmas Eve vs. Christmas Day; keeping strictly kosher for Passover vs. use of the usual dishes, etc.), how do you propose that these differences be reconciled?

When these differences involve family obligations (e.g., "We always go to Grandma's house on this holiday"), how do you propose to resolve such conflicts?

Questions About Secular Holidays

Which secular holidays (e.g. New Year's, July 4th, Memorial Day, Thanksgiving, etc.) do you celebrate? (Note: Valentine's Day has its own section.) Please rank these holidays in order of their importance to you, with "1" being the most important.

Rank	Holiday

Describe your childhood traditions for each of these holidays.

How do you wish to preserve your holiday traditions in your new married life? ______________

When the two of you have conflicts, how do you suggest resolving them (e.g., alternating years, dividing the holidays, spending them apart)? ______________

When there are absolute conflicts over how to celebrate (e.g., New Year's celebrated quietly, as a couple versus with friends, out on the town, etc.), how do you propose they be reconciled?

When these differences involve family obligations (e.g., we always go to Grandma's for New Year's), how do you propose to resolve this kind of problem? ______________

Questions About Valentine's Day

Using the following scale:

Unimportant ... Very Important

1 2 3 4 5 6 7 8 9 10

How important is this day to you?_____

Now please describe your feelings about this holiday. ______________

How do you wish to celebrate Valentine's Day? ______________

Using the same scale, how do you suppose your partner feels about Valentine's Day's importance?_____.
Please elaborate: ______________

To the extent that your feelings about this "Day for Lovers" is different from your partner's feelings about it, how do you propose to meet your partner's expectations? How can your partner best please you? ______________

Vacations

"Marriage must constantly fight against a monster that devours everything: routine." — *Honoré de Balzac*

The importance of taking time off from your routine, work-a-day world to spend "fun" time together is not to be underestimated. Vacation time is important both for individuals and for couples. Vacations provide the opportunity to revive flagging energy levels and to recommit to each other emotionally. Time away from their everyday existence provides a couple with opportunities to rethink their goals and direction and to rededicate themselves to each other. In this regard, recreation time can truly be an opportunity for "re-creation."

Even if you can agree on this in principle, at times it may take considerable effort from one partner or the other to tear themselves away from work, social, community, and family commitments. In addition to embracing the principle that vacations are important, couples need to also agree on how much money and time should be spent on them, where you should go and what you should do (relaxation/education/adventure/spiritual or community-focused activities, etc.), and whether or not to include others, or to make vacations "only for us" time.

SHIRLEY AND JOE

Shirley didn't just like the beach: she was adamant that *all* weekends between Memorial Day and Labor Day would be spent there. Joe had nothing against the beach; in fact, they had met at the shore. It was therefore a very special place for him as well. But every weekend? Joe wanted some variety. He also wanted a vote.

Shirley felt she was a reasonable person on most issues. However, she found herself unsettled when Joe could so easily demonstrate her irrationality in this area. There were also other areas in which Joe hinted at Shirley's less than fully democratic approach to resolving disputes.

What started out as an effort to negotiate a tough issue for Joe and Shirley (vacation plans) became an opportunity for them to address the larger issue of how to resolve their other differences. The more the couple talked (both being careful not to raise their voices), the more they saw the benefit of addressing this issue with the help of a third party.

A psychologist Joe had seen years earlier seemed a practical choice for the couple. By working with him, they learned how to advance their goal of being better able to find compromises, what the therapist called "getting to yes." They also began to enjoy the process of mutually planning their summer weekends.

The following questions should help you start finding out how each of you feels about vacation, where your preferences are perfectly compatible, and where there may be some need for compromise.

Where and how did you like to spend your vacations before your involvement with your partner? ____________________

How often and how long were your vacations? ____________________

With whom did you go on vacation? ____________________

Once married, how do you want your vacation tradition (if any) to change? ____________________

____

How much money do you usually spend on vacation? ____________________

Where do you usually obtain the funds for your vacations? (Check all that apply.)

_____ Savings

_____ Loans

_____ Credit card debt

_____ Gifts

_____ Other ____________________

When on vacation (using the scale below) circle your preferred level of activity.

Sedentary									Very active
1	2	3	4	5	6	7	8	9	10

When on vacation (using the scale below) circle your preferred level of adventure/risk-taking.

Very Safe									Very Risky
1	2	3	4	5	6	7	8	9	10

When planning a vacation (using the scale below) please circle your preferred level of novelty.

Always the Same									Always Different
1	2	3	4	5	6	7	8	9	10

Please describe your ideal vacation. ____________________

____

How important is it that your mate shares this preference? ____________________

What kinds of vacation are most attractive to you?

Location ____________________

Level of luxury ____________________

Duration ____________________

Novelty ____________________

Expenditure ____________________

Amount of travel (distance from home) ____________________

Stay-at-home ("stay-cations") ____________________

What kinds of vacation are least attractive to you?

Location ____________________

Level of luxury ____________________

Duration ____________________

Novelty ____________________

Expenditure ____________________

Amount of travel (distance from home) ____________________

Stay-at-home ("stay-cations") ____________________

Where there are differences, what are you willing to do to accommodate your partner's preferences? ____________________

____

*Your Wedding**

To love another person is to see the face of God. — Victor Hugo

Planning a wedding can be enormously rewarding, even exhilarating. Or it can be annoying, disheartening, or downright intimidating. Is it any wonder that some couples choose to elope (and many others think about it)?

At its best, a wedding can be an opportunity for couples to make a public and, for many a sacred, statement of their commitment to bind themselves to each other "for as long as they both shall live." In that sense, it can be a very meaningful and important time, and event, for the couple.

Unfortunately, to listen to many mothers-of-the-bride or professional wedding planners, you might think that wedding planning is not for the timid, or for amateurs. Sometimes they even seem to think it's not for the bride-and groom-to-be.

Many a spat arises over what can later seem, in the larger scheme of things, to be trivial matters. (Will the groomsmen wear morning coats or formal tuxedos? What will the color scheme be? What kind of music? Buffet or sit-down meal? etc.)

It is not unheard of for a wedding to be postponed or even cancelled over such small, but at the time seemingly significant, matters.

When presented with dilemmas of this nature, you will have choices to make. You can choose to care a bit less about these small differences, keeping your focus on the larger meaning of it all and graciously making concessions. Or you can find ways to keep things in perspective even as you hold your ground.

Some couples conclude (either separately or together) that the wedding is more important "for the family." These couples may be more indulgent about the seemingly irrational stances that overly invested family members may take about some of these issues.

For others, family intrusion into the planning of the wedding may be viewed as an opportunity for the couple to assert themselves as independent, mature adults. You may also feel this is the time to show your family that your spouse-to-be now has the primary position in your life, and that you will need to put his or her needs and desires ahead of your devotion to your parents and other family members. If you do so, it may be the first time in your life that you have asserted your own choices over those of family members or other overly invested individuals. (See "Dreams and Goals" for more on this.)

Regardless of which path you choose, there are a variety of ways to make this ceremony truly your own. Your wedding provides the opportunity for you and your partner to declare to family, friends, and the larger community that you intend to go forward into the rest of your lives as a grown-up couple starting your own family, rather than as obedient children. That doesn't mean that you won't care about or respect your parents' wishes. But it should mean that you are able to work together in planning the details of the wedding in a way that recognizes the marrying couple as entering upon, if not already in, their adult lives.

The exchange of rings, the wedding canopy, the taking of communion together, the breaking of the ceremonial glass, the wedding processional in which the father "gives the bride away," etc., all of these traditions and rituals can play a part in making this statement. How you avail yourselves of this opportunity and how you choose to customize your wedding can add something important about what is uniquely you to the process. Vows you have written yourselves, special songs, details of the music or the wedding celebration, the wedding rings you choose, and other choices you make in this process—all contribute to describing your unique union as a couple.

This is Your Big Day! And while you can let others win some of the little battles—or even the big ones—remember that you and your partner are in this together. Make sure that if there's strife, you and your partner are on the "winning side"—which is defined as "we two, together." Regardless of any concessions you two make, it's the *two of you* making them, together—that is something to celebrate!

RHONDA AND NOAH

For as long as she could remember, and for as long as her family and friends could recall, Rhonda had a picture of just what her wedding would be like. The wedding would be officiated by the rabbi who was present at her bat mitzvah. She'd have her lifelong friends, her new friends, and her large family all in attendance. She'd have a flowing white dress with ornate embroidery. It would be held in the synagogue in which she'd grown up. Her attendants were already named in her head. She had a vivid notion of the menu, the music, the flowers, and other decorations. You get the picture.

Unfortunately, Noah did not. He and Rhonda had met in graduate school. They had similar interests, career goals, backgrounds, and values. However, Noah was a very private person. He felt uncomfortable in large groups and never wanted to be the center of attention. The thought of being in the spotlight as they danced their first dance sent shivers of dread down his spine and even caused him to lose his appetite. This actually happened when, at the caterer's "tasting," the conversation naturally turned to a discussion of the post-ceremony events. Hearing the details was sufficient for Noah to feel queasy.

Noah's discomfort did not come as a total shock to Rhonda. However, she had been assuming that he would be compliant. This was, they both hoped, a one-time event in their lives, and she had counted on her wedding to be "just so." And actually, this is precisely the point Noah emphasized in a psychologist's office...it seemed that their wedding was "her wedding." In successive meetings with the therapist, the couple addressed both Noah's shyness and the implications of the messages he'd been sending to Rhonda about his discomfort with their wedding plans.

It turned out that Noah was also feeling very uneasy about future events with Rhonda's family. He regarded their celebrations as over-the-top. The psychological consultation was not easy for either Rhonda or Noah, but they soon began to re-examine their decision-making process as a couple. Noah began to recognize that his shyness might be a more serious problem for him than he had initially been willing to admit. For her part, Rhonda came to appreciate that not all her girlhood dreams needed to be realized. (After all, she had never gotten that pony in her backyard, and her life seemed to be going just fine without "Pebbles.")

The couple's wedding ceremony and reception details actually fell into place quite easily once these issues were acknowledged and dealt with in a professional setting. Noah worked on his social anxiety and Rhonda began learning to compromise. Would they live happily ever after? Their chances were certainly enhanced by the way they went about solving this dilemma.

Questions About Your Wedding/Reception/Honeymoon

(Reminder. Please feel free to attach additional pages as needed.)

Please describe your ideal wedding ceremony ____________________

____

____

What do you think are the essential elements of a wedding? ____________________

____

In your opinion, what are some of the optional, or less important, elements? ____________________

____

Whom will you choose to serve as your "attendants"? ____________________

____

Whom do you hope will serve as attendants for your fiancé? ____________________

____

Whom do you want to officiate at your wedding? ____________________

Who are the people that you *most* wish to have present at your wedding ceremony? (Here, especially, feel free to add additional pages if you need to.) ____________________

____

____

____

____

____

Is there anyone whom you prefer *not* to have present at your wedding ceremony? ____________________

____

____

Please describe your ideal reception: ____

____

____

What do you think are the *essential* elements in a wedding reception? ____________________

____

____

What, for you, is optional or less important? ____

____

____

Whom do you want to have present at the wedding reception? (You may attach additional pages here, if needed.) ____

____

____

____

____

Is there anyone whom you prefer *not* to be present at the wedding reception? ______________

____

____

Please describe your ideal honeymoon: ____

____

____

What for you are the *essential* elements in a honeymoon? ____________________

____

____

____

What, for you, is optional or less important? ____

____

____

Questions About Auxiliary Wedding Events

Please describe your preferences about the following:

Rehearsal dinner/bachelor/bachelorette party, bridal shower, etc.______________________________

____

____

What, for you, are the *essential* elements in these additional activities or events? _______________

____

____

What, for you, is optional or less important? ____

____

____

Whom do you especially want to be present at these auxiliary wedding events? ________________

____

____

Is there anyone whom you would prefer *not* be present at these wedding events? ______________

____

____

Do you want a legal name change when you marry? Y/N ___ If yes, whose name will change, and to what? ____

How will your children be named—both first and surname? ______________________________

____

Which of the above areas do you think may cause some conflict with your partner? ____________

____

How do you hope to resolve the issue? ____

____

When the Going Gets Rough

"Lots of people want to ride with you in the limo but what you want is someone who will take the bus with you when the limo breaks down." — Oprah Winfrey

Drugs / Alcohol / Tobacco, and Other Addictive Habits

When it comes to the use of mood-altering substances and other potentially ruinous behaviors, if you two are in perfect accord on how much, when, where, and what sort of behavior is acceptable, then you're almost home free.

Please note, I said "almost."

Many couples may have concerns about themselves or their fiancé when it comes to this area that they are reluctant to express. But ignoring any potential problems in this area is not a good idea. It's much better to talk about it now and if necessary get some help and/or clarification of the situation than to allow your concerns to fester—and the behavior to get worse.

Often couples will witness an unraveling of their blissful state as intoxicants and mind-altering drugs, medications and/or other health-threatening activities come to play a progressively larger role in their lives. And things can go from bad to worse when these substances and activities grow to be a part of the day-to-day functioning of one or both partners in a marriage.

Frequently the assumption of the partner of the "user" is that that this behavior is "only a phase" or "he's/she's just experimenting, he'll/she'll settle down once we're married."

Sometimes this happens; much more often, unless it is dealt with proactively, it doesn't. Your concerns can be warning signs, and you ignore these warnings at your peril. Sometimes a professional consultation is appropriate, if only to serve as a precaution and to clear the air.

The grave consequences of what was once an amusing or slightly disconcerting habit that develops into a major, relationship-threatening problem can spell disaster for a marriage, and sadly disaster also for the children born into such a family.

Therefore couples are wise to discuss these issues before they get married. Perhaps the problem is only a difference of opinion about what constitutes responsible, healthy use, and it can be readily resolved. Perhaps not. In either case, getting timely professional assistance is recommended.

Other lifestyle habits that can run the range from mild and harmless amusements to major problems can include gambling, physical risk taking, and Internet use (excessive spending, viewing porn sites alone, excessive time spent on social networking sites, etc.). Here also, self-analysis, mutual disclosure and problem solving and, if necessary, professional consultation, can lead to important growth for both individuals and couples.

DENISE AND PATRICK

Denise was a recent college grad. She assumed that, like herself, Patrick had relied on recreational drugs for unwinding during his undergraduate years. However, this wasn't the case. Patrick knew of the drug scene at school but he was not a frequent user at all. Patrick was not totally disapproving of occasional recreational drug use and realized that many at school who had partaken in drugs turned out to be just fine. They went on to get jobs, go to grad school, or find good volunteer/internship positions. But Denise was getting stoned what seemed to him to be all the time. True, she still held a responsible position as a teacher's aide. But her drug use wasn't solely restricted to weekends. Also, her friends seemed to be even more committed to drug use as a lifestyle than she was. This made Patrick uneasy.

Patrick adored Denise. He was sure that they were meant for each other. Nonetheless, he was growing increasingly troubled by her drug use. She seemed to be embracing this behavior as a preferred source of relaxation. Patrick was also confused. Who had the problem? Was it Denise? Or was he simply too "buttoned-up?" He suspected that some of Denise's friends viewed him this way. Patrick thought frank disclosure and, perhaps, discussion with their priest (who was to be the officiant at their wedding) would be a good way to try to resolve this problem. Unfortunately, Denise took offense at what she saw as Patrick's narrow-mindedness and intolerance of her mode of relaxation. She was also offended by his negative view of her friends' lifestyle. To her, bringing in a third party, the priest (who recommended a 12-step program for Denise), was seen as an unwanted and rather paternalistic intrusion into her privacy.

Denise decided that she and Patrick needed "a break" before proceeding with their wedding plans. Patrick was ambivalent but reluctantly agreed. They eventually ended their relationship because both felt they could never compromise on this issue. Though both regretted it initially, eventually both of them felt good about their mutual decision.

Questions About Alcohol Use

Describe *your* current use of alcohol.

Frequency ____________________

Time and location __________________________

Types of beverages ____

On the following scale, choose a number that describes how you feel about this level of consumption.

Perfectly comfortable Out of control

1 2 3 4 5 6 7 8 9 10

Is this a habit you wish to curtail or discontinue? Y/N ___ If yes, would you welcome your partner's assistance? Y/N ___ If yes, how can your partner help?___________________________

____

____

If yes, what steps will you be taking on your own behalf? ___________________________

____

Please describe what you know about your partner's current use of alcohol.

Frequency ___________________

Time and location _________________________

Types of beverages ____

On the following scale, choose a number that describes how you feel about his or her level of alcohol consumption. ____

Perfectly comfortable Out of control

1 2 3 4 5 6 7 8 9 10

If you find this to be a problem area, how do you wish to address this with your partner?

____

Questions About Illegal Drug Use

Describe *your* current use of illegal drugs.

Frequency ___________________

Time and location _________________________

Types of substances ______________________________

On the following scale, choose a number that describes how you feel about this level of consumption.

Perfectly comfortable Out of control

1 2 3 4 5 6 7 8 9 10

Is this a habit you wish to curtail or discontinue? Y/N___ If "yes," would you welcome your partner's assistance? Y/N___ If yes, how can your partner help? ___________________________

____

If yes, what steps will you be taking on your own behalf? ___________________________

____

Please describe what you know of *your partner's* current use of illegal drugs.

Frequency ____________________

Time and location ___________________________

Types of substances ____

On the following scale, choose a number that describes how you feel about this level of consumption.

Perfectly comfortable Out of control

1 2 3 4 5 6 7 8 9 10

If you find this to be a problem area, how do you wish to address this with your partner?

____

Questions About Prescription Medications

Please describe any personal *overuse* of prescription or over-the-counter medications, if there is any.____

On the following scale, choose a number that describes how you feel about this prescription drug use. _____

Perfectly comfortable Out of control

1 2 3 4 5 6 7 8 9 10

Is this a habit you wish to curtail or discontinue? Y/N ___ If yes, would you welcome your partner's assistance? Y/N ___ If yes, what kind of assistance? ______________________________

____

If yes, what steps will you be taking on your own behalf? _______________________________

____

Describe any overuse of prescription or over-the-counter medications by your *partner.*

____

On the following scale, choose a number that describes how you feel about this prescription drug use. _____

Perfectly comfortable Out of control

1 2 3 4 5 6 7 8 9 10

If you find this to be a problem area, how do you wish to address this with your partner?

____

Questions About Smoking (Including Marijuana)

Do you smoke? Y/N ___ If yes, how much and when? ___________________________

Is this a habit you wish to curtail or discontinue? Y/N ___ If "yes," would you welcome your partner's assistance? Y/N__ What kind of assistance? ___________________________

How does your partner feel about your smoking? ___________________________

If your partner smokes, how do you feel about this? ___________________________

____

Questions About Other Addictive Habits

Please describe other habits or behaviors that are, have been, or may become problematic for *you* (where you have felt out of control).

Excessive spending ___________________________

Excessive Internet use (including pornography and social networking) ___________________________

____

Gambling ___________________________

Other (e.g., nail biting, hair pulling, cutting, talking on the phone, angry outbursts, reckless driving, etc.) ___________________________

____

Are any of these behaviors ones you wish to curtail or discontinue? Y/N ___ If yes, would you welcome your partner's assistance? Y/N ___ If yes, what kind of assistance?

____

____

Do any of the potential behavioral problem areas described above concern you regarding your partner? Y/N ___ If yes, how do you wish to address this problem? ___________________________

____

If your partner has concerns about any of these areas *in you,* how and when would you wish to be approached? ___________________________

Questions About Risky Behaviors

Please indicate any activities which you or your partner regard as risky :

____ motorcycling ____ skateboarding ____ mountain/rock climbing ____ parasailing

____ slack lining ____ car racing ____ martial arts ____ sky-diving

____ other extreme sports/activities ___________________________

Are any of these activities ones you would be willing to discontinue or curtail? Y/N ___

Please indicate which activities, and how you would be willing to adjust them. ________________

____

Are any of these behaviors ones that you would ask *your partner* to curtail or discontinue? Y/N ___
Please indicate which ones, and how you would approach your partner. ______________________

____

How do you propose resolving any problems that arise in reconciling differences around engaging in these risky activities? ____

____

In Sickness and in Health

"In sickness and in health, for as long as ye both shall live..."

Most of us will encounter periods of compromised health at some time during our lives. We also will be called upon to respond to health problems with our loved ones. The way we deal with these inevitable health challenges can be an important area for self-analysis and discussion.

Mental health is as important as physical health. This is especially important to stress because in most societies, sadly including our own, emotional problems are regarded as less real or less worthy of attention and intervention than most physical health problems (obesity is an exception). Mental illness is often viewed with suspicion or as a sign of weakness of character. Because emotional problems are so frequently stigmatizing, it is all the more important for couples to offer each other the support that may not be readily provided by the world at large, and that is so badly needed in order for people to get better.

ELLEN AND PETE

From Ellen's perspective, Pete was, in her words, "a walking cardiac case." She considered him the epitome of poor health habits. He ate and drank indiscriminately, exercised erratically, and wouldn't consult with a physician even when ill. His occasional mishap (a badly cut finger, a bout of gastroenteritis) were handled in a nearby emergency room.

Ellen was of a wholly different mindset when it came to health habits. She believed in careful attention to diet, exercise, and sleep. She had an ongoing relationship with her physician, regular physical exams, and routine tests.

Pete's family was totally sympathetic to Ellen's concerns. However, years ago, they had thrown up their arms in defeat. The couple agreed to talk about this issue in front of Ellen and Pete's prospective officiant, a mutual friend and Pete's former law professor. The professor attempted to bridge the gap. She thought that the problem had two facets: one, Pete's health habits and two, his lack of attention to health monitoring. She suggested that maybe Pete and Ellen could agree on just one modification.

Pete agreed, and chose to see an M.D. and to submit to testing on a regular basis. While Ellen strongly preferred to have Pete change his health habits, she was willing to accept "half a loaf." She recognized that Pete's autonomy needed to be respected. For his part, Pete felt that his concession had merit for the health of the marriage despite the fact that he still believed in his invincibility. Ellen secretly hoped that the new internist would encourage a healthier lifestyle for Pete as well.

All of the questions that follow apply ***equally*** to physical and mental health.

What is the general state of your health? ____________________

When was the last time your health status was evaluated? ____________________

What health problems (if any) do you have? ____________________

____

____

What lifestyle restrictions (if any) does your health status place on you? ____________________

____

____

Do you have a history of sexually transmitted infections or disease? Y/N ___ If yes, please elaborate. ____________________

What part of your health history do you ***not*** wish to share with your partner? ____________________

____

What part of your health status do you ***not*** wish to share with your partner? ____________________

____

What do you feel you need to know about your partner's health history? ____________________

____

____

What do you feel you need to know about your partner's current health status? ____________________

____

____

What do you do to stay healthy? Please describe below.

Nutrition/weight control ____________________

Exercise ____________________

Regular visits to a physician ____________________

Mental health support ____________________

Meditation/mindfulness ____________________

Alternative health providers ____________________

Other ____________________

What health habits do you expect your spouse to practice? Please elaborate.

Nutrition/weight control ____________________

Exercise ____________________

Regular visits to a physician ____________________

Mental health support ______________________________

Meditation/mindfulness ______________________________

Alternative health providers ______________________________

Other ______________________________

How do you wish to assist your partner in health-related matters? ______________________________

____

How much of your partner's health do you consider his or her own responsibility?

____

____

Do you want your mate to help you practice healthy habits regarding:

Nutrition? Y/N ___ Explain. ______________________________

Exercise? Y/N ___ Explain. ______________________________

Other? ________________ Explain. ______________________________

Do you welcome comments on your health status (nutrition, exercise, etc.)? Y/N____ Explain. ______________________________

Would you resent comments by your partner about your health status (nutrition, exercise, etc.)? Y/N ___Explain. ______________________________

Do you forbid comments by your partner about your health status (nutrition, exercise, etc.)? Y/N ___ Explain. ______________________________

How do you behave when you're ill?

___ self-sufficient ___ I fake feeling well ___ I become needy ___ cranky

___ depressed ___ I just want to be left alone ___Other ______________________________

Indifferent — Very Attentive

1 2 3 4 5 6 7 8 9 10

Using the scale above,

How do you react when someone close to you is ill? ____

How do you want your mate to treat you when you are ill? ____

How do you want to treat your mate when he/she is ill? _____

Using the following scale, choose the number that best describes your compliance with your practitioners' advice for maintaining health and with treatment when ill._____

Noncompliant — Very Compliant

1 2 3 4 5 6 7 8 9 10

Using the same scale, choose the number that best describes what level of compliance you would ask of your mate._____

'Til Death Do Us Part

"It is not the length of life but the depth of life..." — Ralph Waldo Emerson

Okay, so this is something no one really likes to think about.

But, of course, death is all around us all the time, whether we choose to think about it or not. Disclosing your own feelings and beliefs about death, even as confused and contradictory as they may be, can lead to greater closeness between you and your partner.

When the time comes, important decisions need to be made—decisions about life-prolonging measures, organ transplants, hospice, and other end-of-life issues. Eventually funeral and burial arrangements or other arrangements must be made. If you have talked with your partner about some of the issues surrounding final illness and death in advance, you can avoid much unnecessary anguish in the years to come.

Cultural habits or religious beliefs may become very important as decisions about the end of life, burial, etc. have to be made. Knowing what your partner's wishes are as well as any family, cultural, and/or religious expectations that may apply can be helpful and very important to know in advance.

MEGAN AND ARTHUR

Megan and Arthur knew it was important to have the serious talk that many couples avoid until it becomes too rushed, too panicked, and too late. They talked about death and dying, as unpleasant as this topic was for them. They discussed what measures, should either of them fall seriously ill, they would wish to be taken in preserving life, and at what point interventions should cease. They even, commendably, went to a website and obtained the proper paperwork for the state they lived in, to have advance health directives available, should such a need arise.

A problem arose, however, when they addressed the question of what was to be done with their remains. While Megan's wish was to be buried with Arthur hopefully many, many decades from this point in their lives, Arthur preferred to be cremated, both for economic and environmental reasons. The couple found "common ground" by agreeing that as time and life circumstances changed they would revisit this issue.

They were certainly pleased to have broached the topic. But it is not always necessary to thrash out all the details and draw battle lines in cases where couples disagree, even about important matters. Wonderfully happy marriages can include unresolved issues, especially where they aren't central to day-to-day functioning. Demonstrating a willingness to compromise in the present creates an atmosphere of trust. This trust makes it easier to table certain topics for future discussion.

What instructions do you wish to give your partner should you be unable to make health-related choices for yourself? ______________________________

____

Is there anyone else whom you would want to be involved in decision-making about your health? ______________________________

____

Whom would you definitely *not* want to be involved? ______________________________

____

Do you have a living will? (This is a document that outlines your wishes regarding life-sustaining measures in the event of serious injury or illness) Y/N ___

After you are married, will you want your partner to be the decision-maker (health care proxy) indicated on your living will? Y/N ___

If yes, please describe what your general wishes are. If no, please explain why you think someone else would better fill that role for you. ______________________________

____

Whom do you wish to designate, or have you already designated, to administer your power of attorney (person designated to sign binding documents should you be, and while you are, incapacitated)?

____

Are there any religious rites or practices that are important to you in the event that you are seriously ill? (Last rites, visit from a member of the clergy, ***no*** visit from a member of the clergy, confession, etc.) ______________________________

____

What are your beliefs about death and the hereafter? ______________________________

____

What provisions do you wish to make for burial, cremation, memorial service or funeral, etc.)? ______________________________

____

Are there any favorite poems, songs, quotes, or other messages you would want to be shared with your family and loved ones at a memorial service after your death? ______________________________

____

What provisions do you wish to make for your loved one (e.g., burial plot, cremation, memorial service or funeral, etc.)? ______________________________

____

What do you wish to include in your ethical will (i.e., your message to loved ones after your death)? ______________________________

____

____

If there are any areas of potential concern or conflict in the above, how can you work to resolve them now? ______________________________

Parting Thoughts

"A successful marriage requires falling in love many times, always with the same person."
— Germaine Greer

So what is this little book all about?

I hope that answering these questions has helped you get to know yourself a lot better, to consider how you will plan to become the person you aspire to be, and how you and your partner will grow together both as individuals and as a couple in the years to come.

This book has been designed to get you to think about your partner in ways that go well beyond the thrill of being "in love" with the wonderful human being you have chosen to be your life partner.

The questions in this book ask you to take stock of yourself as well. If you have shared your responses with each other, most likely you will have seen someone who is very different from you in many ways.

Finding out about your differences is not a danger sign, and certainly not a signal to call off the wedding. Nor does the discovery of these differences give either of you license to devise a secret (or open) strategy to change your partner.

As several of the scenarios in this book have illustrated, it is a mistake to tell yourself that given enough time, your partner will come around to seeing things your way, or that he or she will change in any fundamental way.

Yes, as you grow and mature as individuals and as a couple you will both evolve and make changes. This occurs quite naturally and, in most cases, inevitably.

But ideally the changes you make will not come as a result of either of you manipulating the other. It is to be hoped that any decisions you make, and any eventual concessions to each other (for example, whether to have children, or to put more money into retirement, or to have a more lavish vacation) will arrive through a process of synchrony. (Synchrony is the mechanism whereby the two partners in a couple come to think and live together in greater harmony, as the rough edges between them gradually and naturally become smoother.)

This process is not one of losing one's individuality, but simply changing out of respect for another way of being and learning and growing together. Synchrony is not the same as symmetry, or being alike. Rather, synchrony is the recognition and celebration of, and respect for, differences that leads a couple toward growing together and intertwining their lives, without sacrificing either one's core beliefs, values, and being.

This book asks you to realize that despite your differences, or maybe even because of them, you can love your partner all the more.

This process of self-discovery and discovery of your partner is not a trap to convince you that he or she is not perfect. (No one is!)

Most likely, your responses to the questions in this book will have shown you that you and your partner are not perfectly matched. (Almost no couple is!)

What did I just say? Did I really say that?

Yes, I did. Because despite what your heart, and the various dating websites would have you believe, there is really no such thing as a couple who is "perfectly matched."

Please repeat these words after me and make them your motto: "My partner is not perfect. (Neither am I.) And that's perfectly fine."

Having a perfect partner is not what matters. What matters is that you and your partner have an abiding love and respect for each other.

In marrying you are deciding to join forces with, and live out your life with, your partner. The better you know each other, discover each other's deepest thoughts, feelings, and desires—and make peace with your differences—the more likely you will be able to live together and love each other "happily ever after."

A Few More Questions

Having completed the exercises in the preceding pages, please use the following scale to describe how compatible you feel you and your partner are.

Not compatible									Totally Compatible
1	2	3	4	5	6	7	8	9	10

How fitting do you think you are as a mate for your partner? ______

How fitting is he/she for you? _____

What can you do to raise your compatibility score? ____

____

____

____

What can you ask of your fiancé to raise his/her compatibility score? ______________________

____

____

If you are dismayed by how much discomfort/disagreement this process of self and partner assessment has raised, I strongly suggest you talk about it with your partner. But there's no need to panic. You might wish to also discuss any distressing feelings/discoveries with trusted friends, family, and perhaps, counseling professionals or a member of the clergy. In some cases, a delay in setting the wedding date may be appropriate.

Seeking out premarital counseling does not signal the death knell of the relationship. On the contrary, it can serve as an opportunity for learning valuable skills that you both can bring into your marriage and make use of for many, many years to come.

If this process of self and partner-discovery *does* lead you to change your minds about marriage, that is not a bad thing either, though certainly it would be disappointing at least in the short run.

But even if this happens, the time you have spent learning more about yourself will surely serve you well as you go on into the rest of your life and into future relationships.

You have shown great maturity and foresight by taking the time to work through these questions. Whatever the result of the process of sharing the information you have discovered about yourself and your feelings about your future partner may be, you can be sure that this has been time well invested.

In closing, I'd like to leave you with one more quotation, one that I often call upon in my own marriage, and also urge upon the many couples that I consult with: *"Be of love (a little) more careful than of anything." — E. E. Cummings*

Congratulations for taking this step, and may your life together be a wondrous one!

For future editions, any suggestions you might have for additional topics or questions would be greatly appreciated. You may e-mail them to: LawrenceSank@yahoo.com

Acknowledgments

I wish to thank the many individuals who offered guidance and encouragement through the years in which I was developing this book. They include, but are not limited to, my daughter, Jessica, who tirelessly read through many versions of the manuscript and frequently saved me from hunt-and-peck purgatory. Dr. Toni Clark was a wonderful informal, yet dedicated coach who gently prodded me along the road to completion. Dr. Norman Rosenthal gave me excellent counsel at the inception of this project. My editor, Janet Hulstrand, was invaluable in more ways than can be enumerated as she shepherded this book through many, many iterations. I also wish to thank Nita Congress for her valuable assistance in getting the process going and Laurie Cullen, copy editor, for her finishing touches.

Mostly, I want to acknowledge the efforts and loving touch of my dear wife, Dr. Carolyn Shaffer, who has faithfully encouraged and exhorted; was undoubtedly at times bored to tears; but was also unfailingly cheerful and upbeat, and always there for me through this project in its many versions. To her I am indebted beyond words.

About the Author

Lawrence Sank is a practicing clinical psychologist who lives and works in Bethesda, Maryland. He has earned degrees and fellowships from Brandeis University, Rutgers University, Harvard Medical School, and the University of Wisconsin Medical School, and has practiced for more than 40 years in the Greater Washington, D.C. metropolitan area, with a treatment focus on couples and human sexuality.

Dr. Sank is happily married to Dr. Carolyn Shaffer, with whom he shares his practice. He has two happily married children, a happily married stepson and four adorable grandchildren.

CPSIA information can be obtained
at www.ICGtesting.com
Printed in the USA
FFOW02n1136110515
13300FF

9 781626 527454